THE CHRONICLES OF
TALISLANTA

**By Stephan
Michael Sechi**

*Illustrated by
P.D. Breeding*

Cover Graphics: John Williams and Co., Greenwich, CT
Map of Talislanta: Joe Bouza
City Maps, Paste-up, Proofreading: Patty Sechi
Typesetting: ProType, Greenwich, CT
Typing: Lauren Schnitzer/Wordsmith, Yorktown Heights, NY
Legal Dept.: Joel Kaye
Creative Director: Stephan Michael Sechi

Thanks to Rick Petrone, Simon Shapiro, Grahm and Brad, Fred Dobratz and the Seattle Group, Charley Winton of PGW, David Ladyman of Hexworld in Austin, TX, Danny and Mike from The Compleat Strategist, Ken Canossi and Rapid Repro, and my patient wife (and generally bewildered stepchildren).

Special thanks to Jim Reinwald, ProType.

Dedicated to Jack Vance, pre-eminent author of fantasy and science fiction.

The Far Reaches

Lake Lir

Lake Lansa

- THE SEA OF ICE -

Lake Mv

L'LAL

RHN

L'HAAN

Lake Y'Lal

Lake Rhin

- THE SEA OF MADNESS -

Black Pit of Narandu

Valley of Mist

XANADAS

Mt. Mandu

HARAK

The Iron Citadel

Firefalls

methyst Mts.

THE SHADOW REALM

THE SINKING LAND

Ope Mts.

KARANG

MAZE-CITY OF ALTAN

Dragonrock

The Cerulean Forest

ANTH

Kharakhan Wastes

THE VOLCANIC HILLS

The Variegated Forest

RIN

Maruk Mt. Range

The Greylands

TIAN

Khan Mts.

CITY STATE OF MARUK

Zaran Mts.

River Shan

Straits of Tian

NDS OF ZARAN

NADAN

SHONAN

JACINTE

EL ARAN

The Red Desert

Emperor's Road

THE QUAN EMPIRE

DJAFFA

CARANTHEUM

HADRAN

AL ASHAD

DRACARTA

Bridge at Hadran

ANASA

- THE INLAND SEA -

CITY STATE OF HADJ

Labyrinths of Sharna

CORAL CITY OF ISALIS

RAJANISTAN

Topaz Mts.

IRDAN

River Shan

Ahazu Lands

Sea of Glass

VISHAN

ud People

Emerald Mt.

Jade Mts.

Mangar Isles

The Ghostlands

JUNGLES OF CHANA

THE CRESCENT ISLES

DOMAL

FARADUN

Bay of Cicz

Donango

AL-LAT

Fahn

TARUN

Pana-Ku

- THE FAR SEAS -

NEFARATUS

SCALE: 1 in. = 150 mi.

Map by Joe Bouza

TABLE OF CONTENTS

INTRODUCTION

These are the chronicles of Tamerlin—explorer, self-styled wizard, and obscure author of ancient times. Within, the wizard recounts the tales of his travels throughout the strange and mysterious land known as Talislanta. It is believed that these writings were compiled by Tamerlin himself, who—being inclined towards romanticism—may have enlarged somewhat on the details of his epic journey. Nevertheless, his works are perhaps of some interest, if only for their value as curios of a bygone age.

According to his accounts, Tamerlin spent the greater part of fourteen years exploring the Talislantan continent. During this time he often traveled alone, typically in the guise of a collector of odd artifacts, though there is some evidence to suggest that Tamerlin may have attempted to pass himself off as a quack doctor or charlatan when the mood suited him. On occasion, he was accompanied by one or more fellow wayfarers: the rogue magician Crystabal, a tattooed Thrall warrior named Ramm, a bestial Jaka mercenary called Tane, a beautiful Mandalan savant named Zen, a Druas known to the wizard as Shadowmoon, and Orianos, a swashbuckling sea-rogue, are all mentioned in the chronicles. Sethera, a Thaecian enchantress commissioned by Tamerlin to provide illustrations for his text, may also have had to endure the wizard's company for a time.

As to the land of Talislanta: those scholars who do not dismiss the topic out of hand disagree as to the origins of this otherwise forgotten realm. Some claim that Talislanta existed long ago, perhaps during the legendary First Age of Atlantis. Others, lending even broader scope to their imaginations, cite Tamerlin's chronicles as proof of the existence of parallel worlds or alternate realities. Proponents of the hollow earth theory, avid readers of Charles Fort, and others of similar bent may formulate even more intriguing explanations for the Talislantan texts.

The maps and diagrams which appear in the text were commissioned by Tamerlin, and may be of similarly dubious utility. The city guides in particular seem to have been compiled in a randomly haphazard fashion, and should by no means be considered complete. Rather, it would appear that Tamerlin noted only those features and references which he deemed important, or possibly, interesting. The inclusion of certain less-than-reputable establishments in these city guides may be construed to be an indicator of Tamerlin's habits and preferences, or of those which the wizard ascribed to his readers.

Tamerlin, evidently anticipating the skepticism of future generations of scholars, had only this to say in defense of his work: "As to the authenticity or value of my writings, I leave it to the reader to decide. Know only this: Talislanta exists, for I have been there, if only in dreams."

TAMERLIN'S FOREWORD

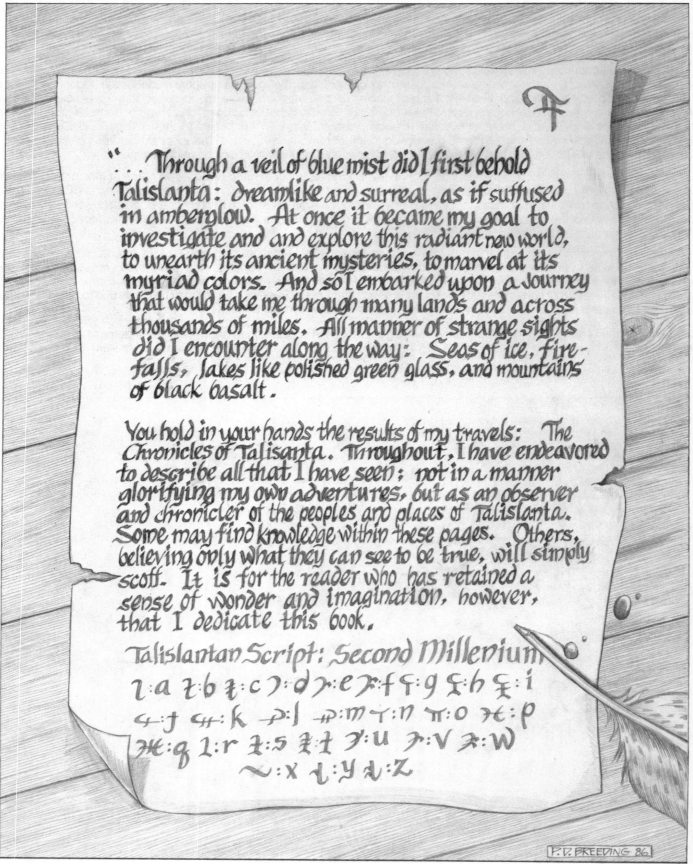

"... Through a veil of blue mist did I first behold Talislanta: dreamlike and surreal, as if suffused in amberglow. At once it became my goal to investigate and and explore this radiant new world, to unearth its ancient mysteries, to marvel at its myriad colors. And so I embarked upon a journey that would take me through many lands and across thousands of miles. All manner of strange sights did I encounter along the way: Seas of ice, fire-falls, lakes like polished green glass, and mountains of black basalt.

You hold in your hands the results of my travels: The Chronicles of Talislanta. Throughout, I have endeavored to describe all that I have seen; not in a manner glorifying my own adventures, but as an observer and chronicler of the peoples and places of Talislanta. Some may find knowledge within these pages. Others, believing only what they can see to be true, will simply scoff. It is for the reader who has retained a sense of wonder and imagination, however, that I dedicate this book.

Talislantan Script: Second Millenium

TALISLANTA: A TRAVELER'S OVERVIEW

To the neophyte traveler or explorer, the Talislantan continent and its surroundings present nearly unlimited opportunities for discovery and adventure. Conversely, the possibilities of disaster are at least as numerous, particularly for those unfamiliar with the many unusual races, cultures and creatures native to this realm. The foreigner is best advised to avoid incautious behavior at all costs; keeping a keen eye out for signs of trouble, tactfully acceding to the customs and beliefs of the natives (no matter how odd or irrational these may seem), and maintaining a degree of civility and decorum in public places. Traveling in groups of trustworthy companions, wielding cogent magics, and/or carrying concealed weapons on one's person are also advisable, unless one prefers trusting all to luck. Other factors which may be of interest to the prospective Talislantan traveler are listed below, as follows:

Currency: The gold lumen, minted to traditional specifications by most of the civilized nations on the continent, is the standard coin of the realm. A single gold lumen is equivalent in value to ten silver pieces, or one hundred copper pieces.

Roadways: Beyond the walls of even the largest Talislantan cities one often finds little but wilderness and intractable terrain. In many such regions, safe and reliable roadways are practically non-existent, a situation which can turn even the most mundane-seeming journey into an exercise in survival techniques. Particularly unsafe is the so-called Wilderlands Road, an ancient and decrepit affair which runs from the eastern border of Kasmir (of the Seven Kingdoms) through the Wilderlands of Zaran and the desert kingdoms of Djaffa, Carantheum, and Rajanistan. Traveling the Wilderness Road is best done in the company of a large and well-armed caravan, this due to the presence of beastmen, Za bandit gangs, and other malicious predators.

In the west, the old Phaedran Causeway is better patrolled, if somewhat haphazardly maintained. The Causeway runs from Zandu through Aaman, terminating at the western border of the Seven Kingdoms. A modest toll is charged at the Great Barrier Wall, which separates the two rival nations of Aaman and Zandu.

The Seven Kingdoms has its own system of roadways, known as the Seven Roads. Aside from its rather unimaginative acronym, the system is of good quality, at least by Talislantan standards. Delays are to be expected at all border crossings, the addle-brained rulers of this confederation of minor city states being unable to coordinate such things as tolls, detours, curfews, and so forth.

The Emperor's Road, which winds its way through the eastern territories of the Quan Empire, is the only thoroughfare on the continent which offers a semblance of security and convenience on a regular basis. Designed and built by subjects of the Quan, the roadway is always well maintained. Foreigners must pay a prohibitive toll of five gold lumens at all bridges and city gates, a stricture intended to discourage traveling musicians, peddlers, and other undesirables from traipsing about the Empire.

Seas and Waterways: The Axis River, in the west, and the River Shan, in the east, are both important waterways, and are used extensively by the peoples of these regions. A number of lesser rivers, lakes, and inland seas are also considered navigable, and are covered in greater detail further on in the text. With the exception of the Imrian slavers, a race of amphibious humanoids, few Talislantan sailors dare to venture into open waters, a phobia not entirely attributable to mere superstition. The various seas and oceans surrounding the continent virtually teem with dangerous creatures and roving Corsair bands. Accordingly, most Talislantan sea vessels navigate by hugging the coastline.

Modes of Conveyance: Aside from the slow but reliable expedient of pedal ambulation, many forms of overland conveyance are available to the Talislantan traveler. In any fair-sized city, there is generally little difficulty in obtaining a mount at reasonable cost. Swiftest of steeds are the creatures called Silvermanes, followed by their cousins, the Snowmane and Greymane. In arid or desert climes, the Ontra, Batra, or Tatra are most suitable. Land lizards, stubborn but powerful quadrupeds from the Wilderlands of Zaran, are best suited to the towing of carriages or wagons. Those of discerning tastes and solvent finances may prefer the comfort of a slave-borne litter or palanquin. In Carantheum, dune ships and land barges are quite popular.

Various types of water craft, some reasonably priced, are available in many parts of Talislanta. Barges and flat bottomed skiffs are ideal for navigating rivers and lakes, reed boats or makeshift rafts often sufficing in places where larger craft cannot go. The finest sailing ships are probably the dragon barques of the Quan Empire, built by the subject Sunra peoples. The Imrians' Coracles, drawn by giant Kra (sightless cave eels), are seaworthy but difficult to manage. The Zandir, Aamanians and Farad make serviceable galleys, though these require large teams of slaves to man the oars. The capabilities of the ominous sailing vessels of the Black Savants, like their mysterious owners, remain largely unknown.

Where methods of land and water travel fail, there is always the possibility of obtaining passage on a windship. Both the magicians of Cymril (of the Seven Kingdoms) and Phantas know the secret of making these wondrous vessels, which traverse the air as sailing ships do the water. They are so costly to make and maintain, however, that few can afford to own such magnificent craft. Only slightly less expensive are crested dragons, which make fierce and loyal steeds if captured and trained while still young. Ungainly and foul-tempered, Dractyl can be found amidst the wastelands of Harak. As the bloodthirsty Harakin tribes also dwell here, it is easy to rationalize not making the long and arduous journey to this isolated region.

AAMAN

Aaman is a land of low hills and wooded glens, bordered to the east by the Axis River and to the west by the Sea of Sorrow. Formerly part of the old Phaedran Empire, Aaman became an independent nation following the long and bloody Cult Wars, which pitted the Orthodoxists against the Paradoxists of neighboring Zandu (see **History of Talislanta**).

The Aamanians are a stern folk, tall and straight of bearing. They have skin the color of cinnabar, with sculpted features and deep green eyes. As required by the arch-conservative tenets of Orthodoxy, Aamanians are taught to refrain from individualistic behavior. Only the most modest attire is deemed permissible: colorless smocks, robes designed to conceal the figure, and caps of starched linen are worn by much of the populace. In order to promote the Orthodoxist ideal of "oneness in body and spirit," Aamanians use an extract of the bald nettle plant to remove all facial and bodily hair, and cultivate a certain sameness of appearance and mannerism. In many lands, they are regarded as the most monotonous folk in Talislanta.

The doctrines of Orthodoxy center around the Aamanians' patron deity, Aa (also known as "Aa the Omnipotent," "Aa the Omnificent," and so on). The tenets of the cult are recorded in a series of iron-bound volumes known cumulatively as "the Omnival." Written over the course of many generations by Aaman's ruling theocracy, the Omnival purports to reveal "the answers to all questions and mysteries; the secret knowledge of Aa; the correct manner of achieving ordered thought; the hundred and more proscriptions against infidels, heretics, witches and the like: what the Omnival does not teach, the true Orthodoxist need not know."

Strict adherence to the inflexible tenets of Orthodoxy dominates life in Aaman. Artisans are prohibited from producing works which in any way deviate from accepted standards. The cubiform structures which pass for Aamanian architecture are all identical in appearance, and their cities are laid out in monotonous, square grids.

Aamanian customs are similarly bland. Conditioned from childhood to conform to acceptable patterns of speech and behavior, Aamanians converse mainly in cliches and axioms. Disagreement with Orthodoxist doctrine is considered tantamount to heresy, and may result in unpleasant consequences. Public displays of affection are forbidden in Aaman, as are intoxicants of any kind. The latter proscription is a particular source of dismay to merchants, travelers and those individuals who must, for one reason or another, spend any amount of time in this tedious and unexciting locale.

The Aamanians have a rigid caste system based upon the acquisition and accumulation of mana, or "spiritual purity." At the head of Aaman's theocracy is the Hierophant, celibate high priest of the realm, who is possessed of unlimited mana. The Hierophant wields supreme power in Aaman, for he is entrusted with sole curatorship of the Omnival. At his decree, the Omnival may be expanded to include such strictures and observances as the Hierophant sees fit to impose upon the populace.

Serving the Hierophant are his representatives, called the Monitors. Only warrior-priests or Archimages who have earned a minimum of one thousand points of mana can attain this lofty status. Each Monitor serves as the ruling prelate of an assigned district, and is responsible for awarding mana points to those worthy of advancement in status, or deducting points from individuals whom they deem unworthy. Many are the sons and daughters of wealthy merchants who have served the theocracy for years.

Next in line come the Aspirants. These individuals are divided into ten "orders," each separated by one hundred-point increments (thus, an Aspirant of the First Order must have earned a minimum of one hundred mana points, an Aspirant of the Second Order must acquire at least two hundred points, and so on). Aspirants who have gained Tenth Order status are eligible for promotion to the status of Monitor, though few ever attain such an exalted position. Individuals who have a mana total of "zero" or less are considered pariahs, and have status comparable to an infidel. In Aaman, all slaves and criminals fall into this category.

Advancement in status is a preoccupation with the Aamanians, who believe that their position in the Orthodoxist hierarchy determines how they will fare in the afterlife. Accordingly, the attainment of mana points is considered of primary importance. The most reliable method of accomplishing this goal, provided one can pay the high cost of tuition, is to enter the priesthood and study to become an Archimage. Temples offering instruction in this field can be found in any city in Aaman.

A less costly means of attaining enlightenment is to join the Knights of the Theocratic Order, the militant arm of the Orthodoxist cult. Attired in shining white armor (actually, black iron plate mail covered with a glossy white lacquer), the Knights of the Theocratic Order serve as protectors of the realm, and are under the direct command of the Hierophant. They are employed in all branches of the army and navy, and may be assigned to travel to distant lands to hunt down and persecute "enemies of the faith" (namely, witches, warlocks and others who do not share the Orthodoxists' narrow-minded views, known as heretics).

Less ambitious members of the cult sometimes find it easier to simply purchase mana by making donations to one of the many temples of Aa found in Aaman. The going rate for this form of enlightenment is one hundred gold lumens per point of mana; a not-insubstantial price, even considering the purported benefits to the soul. "All-seeing eye" medallions, statues of Aa, and other reliquary may also be purchased from the temples, with the same purported result.

Because few Aamanians can afford to acquire mana by such convenient means, the most popular way to achieve elevated status is to undertake a pilgrimage to one of the cult's officially sanctioned holy places. In order of esteem, these are: the Well of Saints, which lies beyond the Volcanic Hills; the Watchstone, situated amidst the Plains of Golarin; the Red Desert in Carantheum;

and several places of lesser repute. Returning with some item or substance native to the holy place is required in order to gain the recognition of the Monitors, who verify all claims and tabulate the accumulation of mana necessary to advance in status.

There are three large cities in Aaman, all of which look much the same. Arat is a port city which once served as a naval installation during the Cult Wars with neighboring Zandu. Aamanian warships are still stationed here, though the facility is now used primarily by merchant vessels. The citadel of Andurin is a center for trade and an important military base. The Knights of the Theocratic Order maintain a sizeable force in the walled city, which is also a popular stopover point for pilgrims headed to the eastern lands.

Ammahd is the capitol of Aaman, and the center of all trade, commerce and culture. The Hierophant lives here in a mighty tower of ivory-colored stone, attended by his most trusted advisors. Far below, thousands of low-ranking Aspirants and infidels toil, loading wagons and canal-barges with shipments of ore and precious stones from Arim. These are conveyed eastward in the caravans of the Orthodoxist ore-traders, as per the Hierophant's dictates. Profits are tallied by the Monitors, and stored for safe-keeping in the Hierophant's tower, which is heavily guarded by the Knights of the Theocratic Order.

Ammahd is located adjacent to the Aaman-Zandu border, and overlooks the most bizarre and spectacular structure in the region: the Great Barrier Wall. Stretching the entire length of the border with Zandu, the wall is an immense stone structure, sixty feet in height and half as wide at its base. It was built following the Cult Wars of ancient Phaedra, a series of religious conflicts that pitted the Orthodixist cult against their bitter rivals, the Paradoxists. After centuries of senseless and bloody warfare, the leaders of the two cults agreed to a truce of sorts. Two separate nations were established: the Orthodoxist state of Aaman, and the Paradoxist sultanate of Zandu. All hostilities were brought to an end in order that each country might rebuild its population and resources, which had been badly depleted by the long war. The two countries then worked together to erect a great wall, bisecting the old Phaedran capitol of Badijan and establishing an official border. Both sides agreed that the Great Barrier Wall (as it was to be called) would be maintained forever as a symbol of the irreconcilable differences between the two nations.

The Great Barrier Wall is open to travelers of all races and nationalities, though a toll is charged at each of its three gates (one gold lumen per person, animal, or conveyance). Proprietorship of the wall and its toll facilities are determined on a yearly basis by a clash of champions. Both the Aamanians and the Zandir expend a considerable amount of effort searching for a suitable champion for the year's match, the outcome of which is worth a small fortune in revenues. There are a few minor restrictions: quadrapeds are barred from competing in the event, as are demons of any sort. Otherwise, practically anything goes.

Held atop the Great Barrier Wall, with spectators on both sides applauding their country's champion, the event is quite an attraction in the region. People from many lands come here just to see the clash of champions, bringing a substantial amount of business to the innkeepers, shopowners, and vendors of both lands. Betting is always brisk, and pick-pockets from neighboring regions consider the event to be something on the order of a religious festival.

Quite inadvertently, I chose Aaman as the starting point for my exploration of the continent. While convenient in an alphabetical sense, this decision proved to be less than propitious. This is not to say that my preparations were, in any foreseeable fashion, unsound. On the contrary: I had in my possession a magical charm which bestowed upon its wearer the ability to comprehend and converse in any language, a scroll of seventeen spells, and a copy of Quistan's "Interdimensional Omnibus"; the latter, a voluminous manuscript detailing the archaic sorcerer's travels throughout the parallel worlds, including his trip to the fabled city of Badijan, in Phaedra. Within were notations on the native culture, customs, and mode of dress, all of which I had studied thoroughly and was prepared to emulate.

Casting a spell of Dimensional Access, I arrived as planned on the outskirts of the city. I adjusted my raiment and, Quistan's Omnibus in hand, proceeded directly into Badijan. It quickly became apparent to me that something was greatly amiss. Gone were the grand concourses, the colorful costumes, and the pomp and spectacle described in Quistan's text. Instead, I looked with disappointment upon a city and people devoid of ornamentation or individuality.

Nevertheless, I decided to try and make the best of the situation. Approaching a comely young woman, I bowed and questioned her with regard to the likelihood of obtaining a room for the evening, implying that a bottle of the local wine and the pleasure of her company would also be welcome. I might stress that this invitation was put forth in a polite and courteous manner conforming in all respects to the accepted Phaedran style.

To have committed a greater number of indiscretions within the space of a single sentence, I now believe, might indeed have been a practical impossibility. The woman drew back as if I were a victim of the plague and emitted a piercing shriek. This drew the attention of three figures arrayed in shining white armor: Aamanian warrior-priests of the Orthodoxist cult, as I would later learn. The ominous looking trio eyed with suspicion my woefully outmoded attire, favoring me with the sort of look generally reserved for condemned felons. I commenced to explain my ignorance of the current fads and customs, but to no avail; the Knights drew silver-plated maces and advanced in a threatening manner.

Forcible conversion to the ways of Orthodoxy (or some equally grim fate) seemed imminent. Fortunately, the timely application of a spell of Bedazzlement rendered the three assailants temporarily insensible. In the interim, I effected a swift retreat into the relative safety of an alleyway.

The local citizenry were unsympathetic to my plight, and gave pursuit. A harrowing chase ensued, during which I eluded capture time and again by the narrowest of margins. I escaped only through the auspices of an Arimite ore merchant, who agreed to smuggle me out of Aaman in return for a promise of three years' indentured servitude. We departed for Arim, I pausing briefly to dispose of Quistan's Omnibus in a nearby sewage receptacle.

ARIM

Arim is a land of rough and irregular hills, interspersed with grassy steppes and thickets of stunted oak and briar. To the north lie the dark peaks of the Onyx Mountains; to the northwest is Lake Venda, source of the great Axis River, fed by countless mountain streams and brooks. West lies Werewood; east, the towering cliffs of Bahahd fall away into the Darklands of Urag.

The people who live in this grey and windy realm, known as the Arimites, are a dour and moody lot. They are swarthy of complexion, with long black hair and dark, deep-set eyes. The men tend to be gaunt and wiry, with glaring countenances and hatchet-like features; the women, heavy-set and lacking in charm. The customary mode of dress in this region defies all concept of fashion, and consists primarily of sackcloth garments, animal hide boots, bulky fur vests, and wristbands, knives, and ear-rings made of dull, black iron.

The Arimites are a humorless people, most of whom live hard lives as miners of the country's considerable mineral wealth. They have no love of song or dance, but favor chakos, a fiery liquor brewed in black iron kegs. Abuse of this potent intoxicant is widespread in Arim, especially among the overworked miners, who seek escape from the tedium of their existence. Even discounting the influence of chakos, violence and other forms of pathologically deviant behavior seem to be ingrained traits among these folk. Accordingly, the Arimites have a reputation in other lands as cut-throats, an assessment which many claim is not entirely without merit.

There are three settlements of note in Arim: the mining and trade center of Shattra, the citadel of Akbar, and the Forbidden City of Ahrazahd. By far the largest of the three is Shattra, a sprawling port city situated on the banks of the Axis River. It is a filthy place crowded with ramshackle wooden structures and perpetually covered in a haze of sooty smoke. Most of the country's mining camps transport their ore to Shattra by wagon, where it is smelted into ingots and shipped downriver in heavy barges. Shattra exports great quantities of black iron, silver, and lead, its primary customers being Amman, Zandu and the Seven Kingdoms. Due to the nature of its business, the city is seldom visited by any save miners and ore traders. The grey-skinned Mongers of Faradun occasionally come here, however, and do a brisk trade in slave girls, courtesans, and concubines; women of grace and beauty are a somewhat rare commodity in Arim, particularly in the isolated mining camps of the northern mountain region.

The citadel of Akbar is primarily a military outpost, though some trade is done here with the nomadic Djaffir merchant tribes. Situated at the southwestern end of a deep gorge which cuts through the Onyx Mountains, Akbar is a foreboding structure built entirely of massive stone blocks. As many as ten thousand Arimite warriors are stationed here at all times, their main purpose being to guard the pass from intrusion by the Ur clans of neighboring Urag. Fully half of this force is comprised of Arimite knife fighters, grim mercenaries renowned throughout Talislanta for their ferocity in hand-to-hand combat. Archers, scouts, and artillerists, the latter skilled in the use of fire-throwing catapults, round out the remainder of the troops at this critical installation.

The Forbidden City of Ahrazahd, located high in the Onyx Mountains, is less like a city than a small fortress. Here, the ruler of Arim, known as the Exarch, dwells in his lofty mountain retreat. Like his ancestors before him, who made their fortunes by selling black iron to the two opposing factions in the Phaedran Cult Wars, the Exarch is a wealthy man. Heavily armed caravans, loaded with chests of gemstones from the mines, are brought to the Forbidden City each month. These the Exarch peruses, keeping the finest stones for his personal collection. The rest are used to purchase the necessities required to properly maintain the Exarch's fabulous estate, his retinue of guards, his slaves, and his royal wizards.

As its name implies, the Forbidden City is closed to all outsiders. Only slaves and employees of the Exarch dwell here on a permanent basis, most of them foreigners. The Exarchs of Arim have long remained secluded from their own people, assigning various subordinates in Shattra and Akbar with the responsibility of governing the country. The Exarch does not dare to set foot outside of Ahrazahd, this for fear of being assassinated by members of the mysterious cult known as the Revenants.

The Revenants are a secret society that specializes in a wide range of covert and often deadly activities. Though murder-for-hire is probably the cult's most lucrative line of business, the Revenants may be hired to carry out almost any act of vengeance, including arson, theft, muggings, threats, and even insults. Anyone who can afford their fees, which range from as little as ten silver pieces to over 100,000 gold lumens, can obtain the services of the cult. This is easily done by the simple method of posting a bill or notice in some public place. The prevalence of the cult is such that a Revenant, attired in customary night-grey cloak and veil, will perform the desired service on a prospective client on the following day.

Government officials, common laborers, merchants, and even jealous lovers and irate housewives have all been known to employ the services of the Revenants in order to settle disputes or avenge affronts to their honor. The popularity of this impersonal (and relatively safe) means of seeking redress is such that, in most parts of Arim, the mere shaking or brandishing of a change purse is considered suggestive of a threat to hire the Revenants.

An example of this unusual custom is provided in the story of the hillman and the chakos merchant, a popular Arimite folk tale. As the story goes, the hillman returned from hunting to find that his wife, in his absence, had come into possession of a full cask of chakos. Having left his mate with funds insufficient to purchase such a quantity of liquor, the hillman became suspicious of the local chakos merchant, whom he believed might be seeking to gain the affections of his wife by plying her with valuable gifts.

Accordingly, the hillman paid the Revenants ten silver pieces to perform a mischief upon the merchant. The merchant awakened on the following day to find his wagon bereft of its wheels, with a note from the hillman warning against further indiscretions. Outraged, the merchant paid the Revenants twenty silver pieces to poison the hillman's favorite steed. This so upset the hillman that he at once gave over fifty gold lumens to the Revenants with instructions to have the merchant thrashed. On the next day, the chakos merchant made similar arrangements for the benefit of his hated rival.

9

CITADEL OF AKBAR

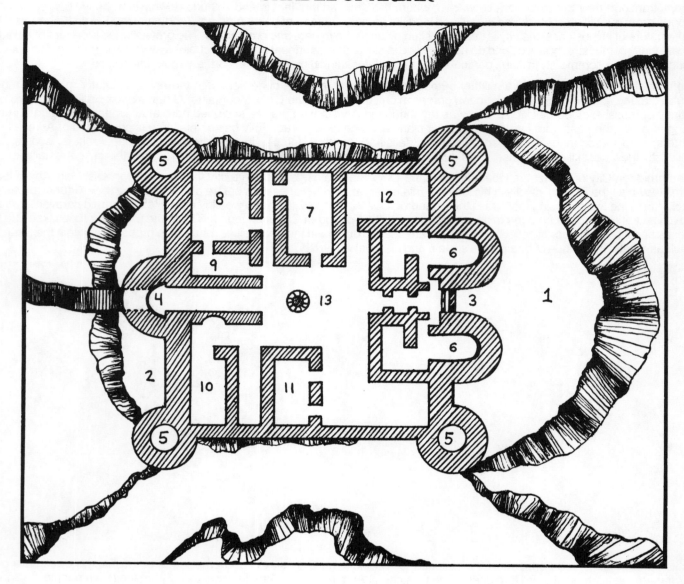

1) The Ridge: The citadel is situated atop a ridge overlooking (and barring access to) the gorge at Akbar, a deep chasm which extends eastward into Urag. Invading armies approaching from the east must travel uphill or scale precipitous cliffs in order to reach the citadel: the former, a difficult endeavor; the latter, a virtual impossibility.

2) Citadel Walls: The walls of the citadel are constructed of massive stone blocks, and stand over forty feet in height.

3) East Gate: Twenty-foot portals of solid black iron bar the way, with a pair of portcullis within.

4) West Gate: A drawbridge, iron gates and portcullis ward the western entrance to the citadel.

5) Towers: Each of the fifty-foot towers includes barracks and armory facilities, except the northwest structure, which serves as a prison for captives taken in battle. Fire-throwers are mounted atop these structures, each of which is manned by a crew of ten artillerists.

6) Gatehouses: Additional barracks facilities and mechanisms to raise the portcullis are found within. Fire-throwers are mounted on the roof of each gatehouse.

7) Requisitioner: Supplies are stored and dispensed from this facility. Merchants and traders visiting the citadel do business here.

8) Dining Hall: A large common room used by troops stationed at the citadel, merchants and traders.

9) Kitchen: Scullery and storage facilities.

10) Stables: Facilities for the citadel's greymanes and visitors' mounts.

11) Armorer/Weaponer: A forge and workshop servicing the needs of the citadel's defenders.

12) Headquarters of the Commander: Here, strategies are formulated for the defense of the citadel, and information gathered by scouting parties is reviewed. Maps of the surrounding territories line the walls.

13) Well

This was the final straw for the hillman, who decided that only the death of his enemy would now suffice to settle their score. While in town posting a notice for the Revenants, the hillman chanced to meet the merchant, who was there for the same purpose. The two antagonists, too bruised and weary to fight and nearly bankrupt of funds, decided to strike a compromise: each contributed half the fee necessary to have the hillman's wife assassinated, thus removing the source of their differences. Relieved to have put an end to their feud, the two men parted friends.

Unfortunately, neither ever saw the other alive again. Unbeknownst to either man, the hillman's wife was a member of the Revenant cult, whose followers are strictly forbidden to do harm to one of their own kind.

The mountains and hills of Arim are home to many species of wild animals, including herds of muskront, wooley ogriphant, and the swift creatures known as greymanes. As predatory exomorphs and yaksha also dwell here, the novice hunter is perhaps best advised to avoid vacationing in this region. Adding to the area's notable lack of appeal are the folk known as the Druhks, a nomadic hill people of violent habits. Similar in physical stature to the Arimites, the Druhks dress in the skins of wild beasts, stain their hair and bodies with the purple juice of wild mountain berries, and wield stone war clubs and jagged-edged, bone daggers. They are decidedly unfriendly, finding great enjoyment in skinning alive individuals who trespass into their tribal lands. Druhk warriors (male and female) ride wild greymanes also dyed purple with berry juice; a most unusual sight, or so it is said.

The Onyx Mountains of Arim are rich in silver and black iron, and are known to hold even more precious substances. Fine emeralds and garnets are found here, as are sards, carnelians, and beryls of passable quality. The caves which dot the sheer faces of the cliffs of Bahahd are known to contain moonstones of immense size and impeccable color. Cliff-dwelling Stryx, wandering bands of Darklings from nearby Urag, and the fearsome Nocturnal Strangler haunt these environs, however, serving to dull the enthusiasm of most would-be prospectors.

BATRE

Batre is a small, tropical isle located to the south of the Dark Coast. Its jungles abound with fruiting trees, crystal streams, and scenic waterfalls. Long a popular stopover point for vessels seeking fresh water and supplies, the island is well known by sailors and navigators, who consider it one of the few safe havens in the Azure Ocean. Batre is even more notable, however, for the race of ivory-skinned humanoids who dwell here, known as the Batreans.

The Batreans are a primitive people who dress in rude garments of coarse cloth and dye their hair with indelible blue pigments. Male and female Batreans bear so little resemblance to each other that they seem to be separate species: the males are huge, slope-shouldered, hairy, and remarkably ugly. Slow and ponderous, they possess the manners of swine, and fight among each other with regularity. The Batrean females, on the other hand, are engaging creatures, slender and lovely beyond compare. Their movements are graceful, and their manner of speech is charming and at times most eloquent. Batrean males seem unmoved by the beauty of their females, whom they largely ignore except during the males' brief, week-long mating season. In fact, it is the peculiar custom of Batrean males to sell their womenfolk for gold, which they horde in secret, underground caches.

For many years, entrepreneuring sea-farers have risked the perils of ocean travel in order to purchase Batrean females, who bring exorbitant prices as concubines in lands such as Zandu, Arim, Faradun, and Quan. Though Batrean males demand as much as 1,000 gold lumens for even the most modest females, their value in foreign lands may exceed five or even ten times this figure.

As for the Batrean females themselves, few evince any great sadness at being separated from their boorish, slovenly mates. On the contrary; some have even been known to help pay for their release with coins pilfered from the hidden treasure caches of their husbands. None appear to miss the mud and thatch hovels which the Batrean males call home, and most seem to adapt to their new surroundings with very little difficulty. Once established in their new residences, more than a few Batrean females have been known to exhibit an uncanny ability to influence their masters by various subtle and effective means, a talent attributed to magic by some observers.

The estimable Kabros, sorcerer and one-time ruler of ancient Phaedra, considered such theories uninformed, and hence, erroneous. In his famed book, "Perception and Delusion," he states emphatically: "The ability of Batrean females to influence males of other species can be attributed to their scent, which possesses aphrodisiac properties similar in effect to tantalus vine. Batrean males, who as a group suffer from chronic sinus difficulties, are evidently unaffected by the potent pheromones emitted by their mates."

Intrigued by Kabros' writings, I endeavored to find some means of putting his claims to the test. An opportunity unexpectedly presented itself in Zandu, where, out of courtesy to a Farad monger, I volunteered to chaperone three Batrean concubines whom he intended to sell in Arim. The Farad went off to tend to other business, leaving me to watch over his wagon, in which were safely secreted his lovely charges. Plugging my nasal passages with two small wads of compacted silkcloth, I entered the wagon, employing a minor bit of legerdemain to foil the Farad's locks.

The Batreans greeted me with obvious delight, and pressed their charms upon me in a most generous fashion. All went according to my most optimistic plans, until a sudden sneeze caused my hastily improvised nasal filters to be expelled. I came to my senses sometime later, awakened by the shrieks and curses of the Farad monger, who had returned to find the concubines missing, and with them, all of his gold. Happily for myself, the Batreans had been kind enough to hide me, dazed but unhurt, in a clump of nearby bushes. I deemed the results of my experiment to be sufficiently conclusive, and departed the area post-haste."

There are two extensive settlements on the island of Batre: the villages of Domal and Lal-Lat. Both are located far inland, and surrounded by hedgerows of thornwood. Crude but effective, these defenses are required to thwart poachers and raiding parties of Imrian slavers, who prefer a more direct method of acquiring Batrean females. Batrean males, armed with giant clubs, patrol the perimeters in slow but fairly efficient fashion.

Passage through the jungle, even along the trails leading to the two villages, is fraught with danger. Wild beasts, and such frightful creatures as the Kaliya (a many-headed, black-scaled species of dragon), are found throughout the isle. Several varieties of lotus also grow here, along with other rare species of plants and animals. To some, the hazards of the Batrean jungles pale in comparison to the potential prifits which may be reaped through acquisition of a few choice Batrean concubines.

BATREAN VILLAGE OF DOMAL

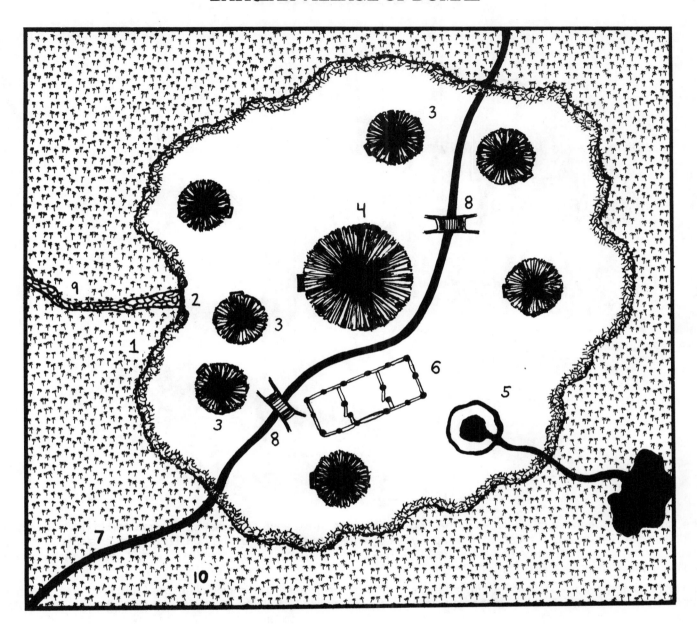

1) Barrier: Encircling the village is a living "wall" of thornwood, augmented by rows of sharpened stakes and hidden snares. The huge Batrean males patrol the perimeter in groups of up to six individuals.

2) Gates: These crude gates are made of sharpened poles lashed together with vines. The nearest hut serves as a guard station.

3) Single Huts: These mud and thatch hovels serve as dwelling places for the slovenly Batrean males. Reed mats are the only furnishings used.

4) Communal Hut: The Batrean females live here in a large communal dwelling. Considerably more intelligent and resourceful than their brutish mates, the females make rugs, hammocks and hassocks of woven raffia, and utilize sun-baked clay pots, vases and wooden utensils. The communal hut is always heavily guarded by males.

5) Garbage Pit: This is a repository for raw sewage and refuse. A narrow trench affords drainage into an adjacent swamp-hole.

6) Animal Pen: Wild beasts, such as marsh striders and jungle dractyl, are kept here awaiting the time when they will be slaughtered for food.

7) Stream

8) Wooden Bridges

9) Path: This is a winding trail which leads northward to the coast. Hidden snares ward against trespass by uninvited guests.

10) Jungle: Dense and forbidding, the Batrean jungle affords numerous opportunities to meet with disaster, including giant leeches, multi-headed kaliya, and the crude but effective snares set by more adventurous Batrean males.

CARANTHEUM

The kingdom of Carantheum is located in the Red Desert, a great expanse of scarlet sand surrounded on all sides by the Wilderlands of Zaran. It is a harsh land, swept by sandstorms and scorched by the burning rays of Talislanta's twin suns. Practically devoid of most forms of life, the Red Desert is nonetheless home to one of the foremost centers of trade on the continent: the Crimson Citadel of Dracarta.

The folk of Carantheum, known as the Dracartans, are tall and jade-skinned, with chiseled features. Formerly a tribe of nomadic wanderers, these hardy folk settled in the Red Desert some centuries ago. With the discovery of red iron (a metal superior in all aspects to common black iron), the Dracartans became rich, and Carantheum soon became an important center of trade and commerce. Once able to afford only the meanest of garments, the Dracartans now dress in flowing robes, cloaks and turbans of fine white linen, and adorn their bodies with red iron necklaces, bracers and torcs.

Carantheum is famed for its thaumaturges, who are greatly esteemed for the wondrous products which they create. Not the least of these is the elusive substance known as quintessence, a crystalline powder derived by a secret alchemical process. By skillful utilization of the magical properties of quintessence, the Dracartan thaumaturges are able to transmute the very nature of substance. Thus, they are able to solidify water, liquify stone or metal, turn sand into glassine stone, or even place elemental forces in suspension. The symbols of the Dracartan thaumaturges' power are the star of four triangles (representing the relationship of the four elements to the three states of matter) and the cadeucus, or "thaumaturgic wand."

The city of Dracarta, also known as the Crimson Citadel, stands as a testament to the extraordinary abilities of the Dracartan thaumaturges. Its towering obelisks and three-fold outer walls are built of solidified desert sand plated with liquified red iron. Merchant caravans from many lands come here, bearing goods of all varieties: amberglass from Cymril, woven goods and hardwoods from Vardune, scintilla and amber from Jhangara, precious stones and metals from Arim, beasts from Djaffa and the Wilderlands of Zaran, and many others. From Astar, the Dracartans obtain much-needed stores of water, solidified and cut into massive blocks, then transported across the desert in sail-powered land barges.

The Crimson Citadel, with its vast riches, is by need heavily fortified against attack. Great siege engines ward the outer walls, positioned to rain quantities of red menace, blue havoc, or yellow peril (liquified flame, ice and sulphur, respectively) on would-be invaders. Smaller versions of these devices are mounted at the prow of dune ships. Like the Dracartans' land barges, these rolling fortresses are sail-powered; added impetus is achieved through the use of wind funnels and storm crystals (solidified wind).

14

The dune ships are manned by warriors of the Dracartan army, known as desert scouts. Mounted on swift ontra and equipped with red iron bracers, vests of red iron discs, swords and hurlants (hand-held versions of the Dracartan thaumaturge's siege engines), the desert scouts are a force to be reckoned with. A dune ship will usually carry up to six dozen desert scouts, half as many ontra stabled below decks, and at least one thaumaturge of some ability. A winch-operated drawbridge allows mounted scout units to enter or exit the ship without delay.

Carantheum is ruled by a king, who is chosen by a process known as the "Test of the Ancients." The ordeal is said to consist of three separate parts: a journey through the desert, the scaling of a magical mountain of glass, and the retrieval of a magic scepter from a vault deep inside the mountain. A committee of nine elder statesmen meets in secret council, selecting three suitable individuals from a list of qualified applicants. The first to successfully complete the test is ordained as king, and enthroned in the royal palace at Dracarta. The remaining two applicants, assuming they survive, are crowned as princes of the realm and granted positions of authority in Nadan and Anasa. The test is held once every twelve years, unless the premature death of a reigning king requires otherwise.

The folk of Carantheum revere Jamba, the mysterious and unknowable god of their nomadic ancestors. They build pyramid-shaped shrines in honor of their patron, whose ways are said to be beyond the understanding of mere mortals. Neither do the priests and priestess of Jamba profess to entirely comprehend the ways of their arcane deity. Most walk about with puzzled looks on their faces a good deal of the time. According to legend, it was Jamba who guided the Dracartans into the Red Desert and aided them in discovering the lost art of Thaumaturgy. Although Jamba has been somewhat lax in the working of miracles since then, he is still well thought of by most of the people of Carantheum.

The Dracartans count as their friends the Djaffir (cohorts during their ancestors' early days as nomads) and the various peoples of the Seven Kingdoms. Carantheum's enemies, on the other hand, are somewhat more numerous. The Necromancers of Rajanistan blatantly covet Carantheum's riches, and have launched attacks against the Dracartans in the past. Though none of these assaults has met with any degree of success thus far, monomaniacal Khadun has sworn to annihilate Rajanistan's Carantheum at any cost. To the east, the Sauran tribes of the volcanic hills are a threat from time to time. The Quan Empire is also believed to have an overly acute interest in the Red Desert region, as does the mercantile nation of Faradun.

Travel to Carantheum, despite efforts to improve conditions, remains a rather perilous proposition. From the east, the only practical routes lead through territories claimed either by the Saurans or the fanatical Rajans. The ancient Wilderlands Road, sole causeway between Carantheum and the western lands, is beset by bandits, wild beasts, and other dangers. As such, the safest means of traveling to Carantheum is in the company of a large, well-armed caravan.

While engaged in an ill-advised search for the sarcophagus of an ancient Dracartan thaumaturge, I chanced to encounter one of the more insidious dangers inherent to the deserts of this region. The rogue magician Crystabal had volunteered to lead the expedition, the first of many mistakes we would make on this journey. In short time, we were hopelessly lost, a sudden sandstorm and Crystabal's overestimation of his abilities having contributed in equal part to this predicament. Our supply of water was diminishing at an alarming rate when further ahead, we spotted an oasis surrounded by swaying date palms.

With newfound vigor, we made for the shaded desert haven. Crystabal, eager to vindicate himself, took the lead. He knelt to drink at what seemed to be a cool spring, and suddenly found himself in the grasp of two hideous, horned humanoids. Fortunately, the rogue magician's swordplay exceeded in skill his talents as a guide, and with help from others in the group, the monsters were dispatched. The oasis faded from sight at the same time, however, causing our party the greatest dismay.

The arrival of a band of nomadic Djaffir merchants happily served to reverse our fortunes. From the Djaffir, we learned that the creatures who had assaulted our party were Sand Demons; vampiric monsters who hide in the dunes, creating mirages and other illusions to lure unsuspecting victims closer to their lairs. We all felt lucky to be alive, and were in similar agreement with respect to the termination of our incompetent guide's employment.

THE CITY OF DRACARTA

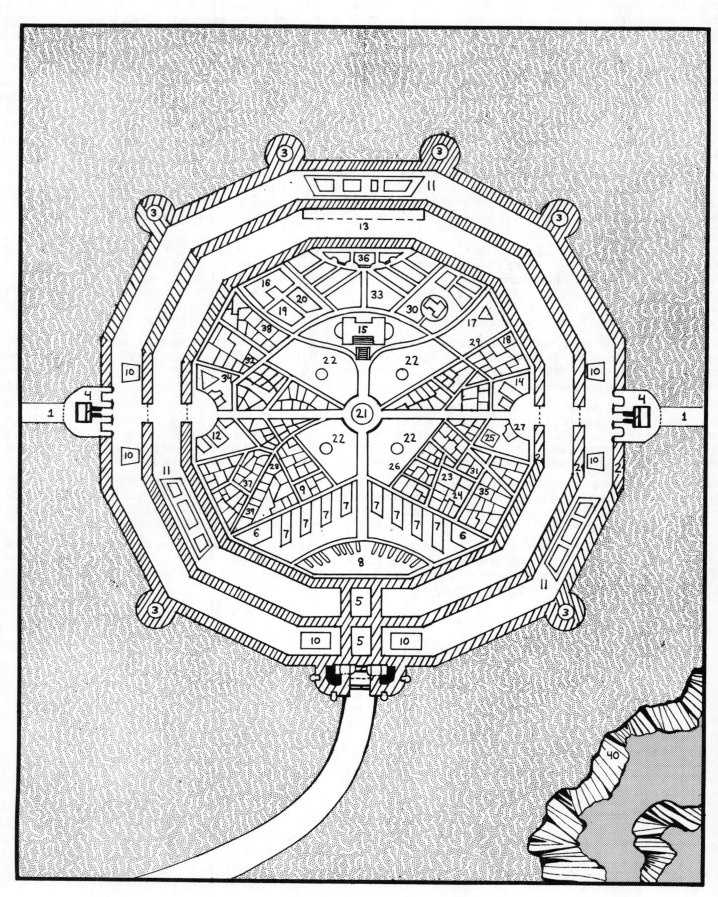

CITY OF DRACARTA

The crimson citadel of Dracarta is the capitol of Carantheum, and the most important trade center on the continent. The city is renowned for its thaumaturges, who utilize their unique talents to produce a variety of useful commodities: red iron, a superior metal derived from the ore-rich desert sand; liquid metals for plating, devices for propelling duneships, and numerous efficacious mixtures and substances. Merchant caravans from many lands come here, bearing goods of all description to trade for the Dracartans' wares. In return, the Dracartans receive goods and materials which are scarce or impossible to obtain in their own land: herbs, spices, burden beasts, timber, fabrics, foodstuffs, and water—a precious commodity in this region.

Dracarta is a striking city, its tri-fold walls and towers plated with red iron, its roadways paved with white stone. The jade-skinned people who live here are friendly, if somewhat reserved; frivolity is not a quality generally associated with Dracartans. Still, the populace exhibits an admirable degree of tolerance for the ways and beliefs of other folk, except as pertains to the inhabitants of Faradun, Quan, and Rajanistan. The former two, while accorded a modicum of courtesy in Carantheum, are regarded with a mixture of suspicion and distrust. The prevailing attitude towards Rajans is less indistinct, and can be categorized as "murderous."

Among the more unusual sights in this region are the Dracartan duneships and land barges. These vessels skim across the desert on red iron runners, braving the hazards posed by sandstorms, hostile bandit tribes, and the scorching suns. Sails are used to provide impetus, augmented by wind machines; devices resembling coils of metal tubing, which are powered by storm crystals (the experience of sailing on dry land is one which particularly appealed to the author, a self-admitted aquaphobe).

The laws of the kingdom of Carantheum are strict, but fair. Individuals convicted of minor offenses are sentenced to a period of hard labor, typically entailing some sort of civic duty (such as cleaning municipal sewage receptacles). Banishing criminals to the Wilderlands is also popular. Worse punishments exist, as described further on in the text.

1) The Wilderlands Road

2) City Walls: The tri-fold walls of the city of Dracarta stand over forty feet high and are plated with red iron. A system of conduits built into the walls allows quantities of red menace (liquified fire) to be rained upon would-be attackers from various strategic points.

3) Towers: Each of these four-story structures is equipped with a large siege-hurlant (mounted on the roof) and a mechanism used to disperse cauldrons of red menace through ports in the outer walls. A crew of eight artillerists operates the hurlant, and a low-level thaumaturge and two apprentices are employed to handle each of the fire-mechanisms.

4) City Gates: The gates to the city of Dracarta are made of solid red iron, and flanked by twin gatehouses. A platoon of twenty sentinels is assigned to each. Squads of ten sentinels patrol the walls, completing one full circuit in about an hour. It is customary for sentinels stationed at the outer gates to perform cursory inspections of incoming cargoes, assisted by functionaries of the Ministry of Commerce (see #6).

5) Channels: The channels are walled entranceways used by duneships and land barges visiting or departing from the city. A network of drawbridges controls access and egress. Security here is as per the city gates.

6) Ministry of Commerce: Offices of the Minister of Commerce, whose duty it is to monitor and register all incoming cargoes of goods and exports. Agents of the Ministry are empowered to seize suspicious cargo or contraband and to make arrests, as warranted.

7) Warehouses: Goods confiscated by the Ministry of Customs are stored here, along with the wares of legitimate merchants.

8) Desert Harbor: A docking area for duneships and land barges. Facilities for maintenance and repair are also located here.

9) The Dune-Sailors' Inn: An inn and tavern frequented by the crews of visiting duneships and land barges. News from the Dracartan citadels of Anasa and Nadan can be had here, though casual visitors are best advised to steer clear of this establishment, which features a generally rowdy clientele. Prices are about average, comparable in most instances to the quality of services afforded.

10) Barracks Complexes: Each of these structures houses a contingent of forty sentinels, twenty artillerists, and ten engineers (assigned to the maintenance and repair of the citadel's fortifications and siege engines).

11) Military Bases: These fortified structures serve as training centers and bases of operations for the Dracartan military. Over two thousand desert scouts and support personnel are stationed at each, including armorers, engineers, and thaumaturges employed by the military. Stables capable of housing up to a thousand aht-ra are maintained in an adjacent facility.

12) The Hurlant: A tavern frequented mainly by members of the Dracartan military and usually avoided by the general public. Patrols fresh from tours of the Wilderlands often come here to unwind, with fairly predictable results. Entertainment is occasionally provided by troupes of Bodor musicians, few of whom will take work in this establishment unless none else is available.

13) Stables: This large facility is open to the general public, and is regularly employed by visiting merchant caravans and travelers. Costs are average.

14) The Red Desert Inn: An inn and tavern frequented by diverse sorts: Djaffir traders, Yitek tomb robbers, Maruk dung-merchants, Danuvian swordswomen, wandering Rahastran wizards, and (less commonly) Farad mongers and procurers. Dancing girls, jugglers and musicians provide entertainment and lend a festive air to the proceedings. The establishment's owner, Samahd, is a retired Djaffir merchant who has traveled much of the continent and is known as a story-teller of seemingly endless capacity. The prices are reasonable, and the accommodations approach excellence in most regards. Especially recommended is Samahd's mochan, an invigorating Djaffir beverage served steaming hot from brass samovars.

15) The Crimson Palace: Dwelling place of the King of Carantheum and the royal family, the Crimson Palace is a magnificent structure built of sandstone blocks and plated with red iron. In the great hall, the King meets daily with his Council of Elders, a group which includes representatives from the military, the Ministry of Commerce, the Academy of Thaumaturgy, the Halls of Justice, and others. A hundred Dracartan sentinels guard the palace and grounds.

16) The Archives: This cavernous structure houses an uncountable number of books, scrolls and tablets, and serves as a library and hall of records for the Dracartan people. Much of the material contained within is accessible to the public through arrangement with any of the seventy-odd archivists employed here.

17) The Academy of Thaumaturgy: One of the most renowned institutes of magic in Talislanta, the Academy of Thaumaturgy is a vast pyramidic structure over one hundred and forty feet in height. The curriculum features courses in alchemy, metaphysics, and the secrets of the art of thaumaturgy: the distillation of elemental essences, the transmutation of substance, the concocting of the marvelous substance known as quintessence. Only citizens of Carantheum may apply for entrance to the Academy's seven-year program, though a series of lectures and symposiums is available to visitors from other lands. Tuition is seven hundred gold lumens per year. A nominal fee of five to ten lumens is charged for most lectures.

18) The Thaumaturge's Crucible: An inn and tavern catering to students and faculty of the Academy of Thaumaturgy. Discourse on subjects relating to the Academy and its curriculum is commonplace, occasionally enlightened by a heated debate or disagreement of some sort. Otherwise, the atmosphere is a bit too low-key for most people's tastes. The prices are (in the author's estimation) too high to support the quality of services available here, though the private booths are not without certain practical purposes.

19) The Halls of Justice: Here the Council of Elders, Dracarta's esteemed legislative body, holds sway, handing down rulings on all matters pertaining to the laws of the land. Individuals accused of wrongdoing are tried in these halls; if found guilty, offenders may face a period of enforced labor, banishment to the Wilderlands of Zaran or—for truly heinous offenses—a sentence of "retribution" (see #36) or immersion in red iron. Under extraordinary conditions, the Council is empowered to remove a reigning king who fails to meet acceptable standards of behavior and ethics.

20) Hall of Infamy: Here are arrayed the worst and most despicable criminals in Dracartan history; their bodies preserved by immersion in liquified red iron, the statue-like forms standing as a warning to future offenders. Among the most notable: the second Khadun of Rajanistan, who led an unwarranted attack against Carantheum in the year 445; the dreaded Sados, reincarnated torturer-king of ancient Quaran; and Xargn, a renegade thaumaturge punished for his unconscionable crimes against the Dracartan people. A popular tourist attraction, the Hall of Infamy is open daily to the general public. An admission fee of one silver piece is charged, the proceeds being used for maintenance of the hall.

21) The Traders' Market: An open-air marketplace frequented by merchants and traders from across the continent. Some of the more common wares include aht-ra (all three species) from the desert kingdom of Djaffa, land lizards, red iron ingots, land dragon hide from Kharakhan, cloth, timber, mochan, dried dates, red iron blades, duneship and landbarge accessories, and antique artifacts from the city of Hadj and the labyrinths of Sharna. Prices vary considerably.

22) City Wells: The city's water supply is stored in underground cisterns, accessible by means of closely-guarded conduits and aqueducts. Water is a precious commodity in Dracarta, and wasteful use of this resource is a criminal offense. Deep wells provide part of the populace's needs, augmented by shipments of thaumaturgically solidified water conveyed in large blocks from Lake Zephyr, in Astar of the Seven Kingdoms.

23) Metallurgist: A sizeable establishment utilizing thaumaturgic techniques to work metals of many sorts. Specialties include red iron plating, jewelry and blades, all at the best prices due to the abundant supply of this useful metal (see #24).

24) The Forges: This extensive installation is owned and operated by the kingdom of Carantheum. Here the Dracartan thaumaturges turn sand to stone and extract red iron ore from the desert sands. The stone is rendered into many practical shapes: columns, blocks, spheres, and arches. For convenience, the ore is smelted into ten, twenty and fifty-pound ingots. Land barges loaded with ingots depart for Anasa, Nadan and the western lands on a weekly basis.

25) Caravan Supply: This establishment features all manner of new and used equipment for the caravan trade, including burden beasts, wagons, tents, and even land barges and duneships. The owner, a former Dracartan desert scout, will accept second-hand and barter goods in exchange for his wares. It is sometimes possible to arrange for passage with caravans heading to Hadj, Danuvia, Maruk or the western lands through the auspices of this establishment.

26) Cartographer: A small shop specializing in maps of the local environs, the Wilderlands, the Volcanic Hills, the Sinking Land, and other regions. Prices range from as low as five gold lumens for a common map to over ten thousand gold lumens for especially rare or unusual charts. The shop's owner (an aged Dracartan scholar who claims to have studied for a time under the savants of Xanadas) can be hired to authenticate obscure maps and schematics. The cost of this service ranges from twenty to two hundred gold lumens, depending upon the amount of research required.

27) The Red Desert Inn: An inn and tavern catering to the caravan trade. The decor is appropriate: colorful tents serve as rooms, the floors are covered with sand, and the large common room is ringed with potted palms. It is often possible to find caravan masters, draymen, mercenary guards and drivers who are looking for work, or to hire on with a caravan of one sort or another. The quality of the inn's services is adequate at best, hardly sufficient to justify the somewhat steep prices; the owner, alas, is a miserly Kasmir money-lender.

28) Four Winds Travel Company: This is little more than an expanse of sand and a single, small building. It is supposedly possible to arrange for passage via windship through this often-abandoned establishment, which is owned by a pair of partners from the city of Cymril in the Seven Kingdoms.

29) The Cadeucus: This is a small shop specializing in thaumaturgical paraphenalia, alchemical apparatus and magical mixtures. The owner, a retired Dracartan thaumaturge, has an avid interest in antiques and collectibles. Used goods are bought and sold here, and prices generally tend to be within reason.

30) Thaumaturge's Guild: A guildhouse and hostel for Dracartan thaumaturges. Material components are sold here at a discount of 25% to Guild members, who may use Guild facilities (library, workrooms, private rooms and studies) at a cost of just ten gold lumens per day. The Guild's registry service lists all dues-paying members, their current status (employed or not) and special fields of interest. Membership costs five hundred gold lumens per year, to qualified applicants only.

31) Armorer/Weaponer: A family of Dracartan ironsmiths owns this shop, which specializes in red iron weapons and armor. They will custom-make any piece to order (double prices for such work), and offer red iron armor and weaponry in a wide variety of styles and types. The quality of their work is reputed to be unsurpassed in the region, and their prices are well within reason.

32) Clothier: This is a reputable establishment offering apparel suitable for arid and desert climes. Styles include Dracartan, Djaffir, Hadjin, Kasmir, Farad and Yitek. Custom work is available at double the usual prices, which are somewhat above average.

33) Memorial Park: This is a natural oasis decorated with statues commemorating the Dracartans' nomadic ancestors, who founded the kingdom of Carantheum. Swaying palms and shaded dunes lend a peaceful and serene ambience to the park, which is frequented by individuals from many parts of the kingdom.

34) Temple of Jamba: A great, pyramidic structure dedicated to the mysterious god of the Dracartans. It is customary for worshippers and priests of Jamba to maintain silence while within the temple, lest some utterance of Jamba go unnoticed.

35) Carantheum Imports: An odd establishment which bears no little resemblance to an indoor junkyard. The owner, a former Maruk dung-merchant, is justly renowned as a collector of oddities, trinkets, geegaws and bric-a-brac; most seemingly bereft of any redeeming virtues. Occasionally one uncovers a find of some sort amongst the bizarre items which litter this shop, but not often. Still, hope springs eternal in the hearts of the many tourists and would-be collectors who visit this shop, many of whom are drawn by the fact that no item in the place is ever priced above ten gold lumens.

36) Amphitheater: This is a large arena seating up to twenty thousand where exhibitions of skill are held once each week. Some of the more popular events include: contests pitting one or more warriors against a dangerous beast, team wrestling (from atop a raised podium), battles between armored land barges, exhibitions of thaumaturgic skill, challenges (non-fatal duels for prize money), and—a particular favorite—"retribution"; the latter, an often ingenious contest pitting a condemned felon against some sort of hazard appropriate to the crime which he or she committed. Admittance is one gold lumen for adults and one silver piece for children.

37) Embalmer: Here the deceased are prepared for burial. As is the custom in Carantheum, the bodies of the dead are thaumaturgically treated to prevent decomposition, placed in stone sarcophagi and interred in the desert. Costs range from one to ten thousand gold lumens, depending on the type of sarcophagus desired. The embalmer traditionally handles all arrangements, including purchase of the sarcophagus.

38) Office of Taxation: Also inevitable are the demands of this institution, which collects a tithe or ten percent of each citizen's annual income.

39) The Catacombs: A gloomy inn and tavern frequented by Yitek tomb robbers, grave-diggers, embalmers and members of the Dracartan military's "corpse squad" (Yitek mercenaries who help clear battlefields in return for exclusive scavenging rights). The common room and private chambers are located below ground amidst a morbid, mausoleum-like setting. Prices and quality are said to be about average.

40) The Mountain of Glass: Site of the legendary "test of the ancients," where prospective applicants for the position of king of Carantheum are put to the test. Secret passageways, traps and other features are updated as needed, so that no two tests are ever alike.

THE CRESCENT ISLES

Regrettably, an aversion to unreliable sea vessels and deep waters kept me from visiting many of the islands which lie in the waters surrounding the Talislantan continent. It was fortunate indeed that, while staying for a short time in the port city of Zanth in Zandu, I met Orianos in a seaside tavern.

Originally from the tiny island of Gao-Din, Orianos was a thief by profession, a fact which he readily and even proudly admitted to me. When I met him he was dressed in the veiled robes of a Farad procurer, though he did not choose to reveal his reasons for doing so. We sat drinking wine and talking for several hours, during which time he told me many tales of his travels with the Sea-Rogues of Gao-Din. In turn, I told him of my plans to explore the continent, at which he suggested that perhaps we might chance to meet again in the course of our travels. We drank a toast and wished each other luck in our respective endeavors.

At this, Orianos excused himself, saying that he would return momentarily after performing a brief but necessary ritual. I waited, however to no avail. Finally, at the insistence of the tavern owner, I settled our account and took my leave; poorer in some respects, but richer with regard to my knowledge of the islands and seas of Talislanta, a portion of which I now reveal to the reader:

The Crescent Isles are a chain of small islands located in the northern reaches of the Far Seas. Many are small and relatively insignificant atolls, appearing on no known map or sea chart. Some, ages-old coral reefs or mounds of water-worn stone, are barely visible above the waves, and are a hazard to all but the most experienced or prescient navigators. Those islands of note, whether in fact or sailors' legends, are delineated in the following text:

Pana-Ku is a volcanic isle, wreathed in jungle and ringed by a dozen or more reefs and lesser atolls. The isle is home to the Na-Ku, a folk of horrific appearance and habits. Tall and angular, the Na-Ku have indigo-blue skin, yellowish eyes, and gaunt, skull-like visages. Both the males and females are fanged, and have clawed hands, hunched torsos, and serpentine tails. Among the most evil of the humanoid races, the Na-Ku are cannibals who relish eating their victims alive. They revere Aberon, the self-proclaimed ruler of all Talislantan demons, and erect massive stone effigies in his honor. Armed with poison-arrows (made from the branches of the venomwood tree, a rare species found only on Pana-Ku), the Na-Ku prowl the waters surrounding the Crescent Isles by night. They prey on humanoid beings of all sorts, whom they take alive and bring back to their island domain. There, at the base of the isle's largest volcano, the Na-Ku hold grisly feasts presided over by their king; a horrible half-demon, fattened on the living prey fed to him by his vile subjects. It is said that the king of the Na-Ku sits upon a throne studded with rare black diamonds, though confirmation of this tale would seem an endeavor best suited to those whose thirst for adventure is exceeded only by an utter lack of concern for their personal well-being.

Fahn is a beautiful island, considered a veritable paradise by those who have visited there. It is populated by a tribe of frail, albino humanoids known as the Sawila. The Sawila dwell in huts cleverly made of woven vines, which, suspended from tall trees, sway gently in the wind. A primitive and peaceful folk, they wear elaborate costumes of colorful feathers, designed to protect their fair skin from the rays of Talislanta's twin suns. Song and dance are integral facets of their culture, which forbids the use of violence for any reason. The Sawila are preyed upon by the cannibals of Pana-Ku and by slavers from the far-western isle of Imria. The lovely Sawila females are valued as courtesans, and bring as much as two thousand gold lumens each in some lands. The only defenses which the Sawila employ against such threats are their enchanting songs, which possess the ability to effect changes in the weather, among other things.

Donango is a peaceful seeming isle similar in appearance to Fahn. In fact, less-than-expert navigators have been known to mistake this island for its placid counterpart. As Donango fairly seethes with hordes of sea demons, such errors seldom go unnoticed for any great length of time. The sea demons of Donango are known to scavenge treasure from the sunken hulks of ancient ships, which they keep hidden in caves scattered throughout the jungle. Certain adventurous types (most lacking in what is commonly referred to as "intelligence") have sometimes been known to come here in the hope of making their fortune.

The **Mangars** are a cluster of four small islands located in close proximity to one another. Covered in jungle, the hidden lagoons and grottos on these islands are home to numerous small pirate bands, known collectively as the Mangar Corsairs. Justly renowned as murderers and cut-throats, the Mangar Corsairs are the bane of ships that must traverse the waters of the Far Seas. There are a number of different bands, all rivals to some degree. In lean times they prey on each other, occasionally fighting over potential plunder. The make-up of these bands is often quite diverse; slaves stolen from Imrian vessels, shanghaied sailors, exiles from foreign lands, and even Chana witchmen have been found amongst the crews of the dark-skinned, shaven-headed Mangar. Like most sensible sea-farers, the Corsairs of this region steer clear of Nefaratus, giving the Black Savant's eerie vessels a wide berth. Neither will the Mangar Corsairs harass the Sea-Rogues of Gao, with whom they share certain common interests. The Corsairs have no such agreement with the bestial cannibals of nearby Pana-Ku, whose dugout canoes they destroy at every given opportunity. The sleek-hulled carracks employed by these piratical folk are arguably among the swiftest of Talislantan watercraft, and should be avoided at all costs.

THE DARK COAST

To the south of the wilderness of Zaran lies the region known as the Dark Coast. Hemmed in to the north by the low-lying Topaz Mountains, the terrain here is predominantly thick and tangled jungle, interspersed with sections of marshland and tropical forest. The Boru and Kiru Rivers effectively divide the land into three separate territories: the Western Rain Forests, home of the Green Men; the Central Swamplands, home of the Mud People; and the Eastern Junglelands, home of the fierce Ahazu.

The Green Men are peaceful beings, small in stature, with skin, hair, and eyes all of varying shades of green. They dress in abbreviated garments made of woven mosses, and make their homes in the boles of great, living plants (called D'Oko). The language of these simple folk is most pleasant to the ear, being reminiscent of the music of wooden flutes. They have a symbiotic relationship with many types of plants, which they tend with great care and affection. In return, the Green Men derive all that they need to survive in the Rain Forests: shelter, clothing, and sustenance.

The Green Men are often preyed upon by slavers from Imria, who invade their domains in numbers during the rainy season (when the Green Men's young are just beginning to mature; Green Men reach adulthood in about six months' time). As they do not employ weapons of any sort, the Green Men are highly vulnerable to such raids. Their only defenses consist of a variety of ingenious snares and pitfalls, which they excel at making. Many of these devices employ living plants, such as the yellow stickler, stranglevine, and violet creeper, none of which ever molest the Green Men. When threatened, the Green Men usually flee into the jungles in order to subject pursuers to their cleverly laid traps. They will not engage in physical combat, however, and surrender without a struggle if caught or cornered.

Although Imrian slavers usually find the capture of the forest folk to be no simple matter, the demand for Green Men slaves (who are docile in captivity, and make superior servants and gardeners) is high enough to warrant the risks involved in their capture. Curiously, the neighboring Mud People and Ahazu tribes will never harm one of the Green Men, believing that doing so will arouse the wrath of the jungle itself.

The Mud People of the Central Swamplands are a brutish folk, squat of build and covered with folds of loose, brown skin. They have four legs, heavy tails, and toad-like visages, and are very strong. The Mud People live along the banks of the Boru River, and consider the territories between the two rivers to be their ancestral breeding grounds. Their dwellings resemble great, oozing piles of mud (hence their name) connected by above-ground tunnel complexes. The language of these creatures consists mainly of grunts and gurgling sounds, said to be almost impossible for other humanoid beings to replicate.

The Mud People are the sworn foes of the Ahazu, their neighbors to the east. They frequently engage their hated enemies in the Swamplands, and sometimes launch raids into the Junglelands which lie beyond the Kiru River. Their favorite weapons are the bwan (a heavy club lined with rows of six-inch long thorns, made from the stump of the thornwood vine) and thorn daggers. At close range, these powerful creatures will sometimes drop their weapons and attempt to rend opponents with their webbed claws, butt them to the ground, and trample them underfoot.

The Mud People fear the Imrians, who venture into their territories in reed boats. As they are somewhat slow and cumbersome, these swamp dwellers are often easy prey for the Imrians' nets and capture-poles. Despite their aggressive nature, the Swamp People are easily cowed when taken into captivity. They are valued primarily for their strength, the Imrians employing the Mud People as slave laborers in the lagoon city of Kragan.

The Ahazu of the Eastern Junglelands are the fiercest of the Dark Coast's inhabitants. These four-armed humanoids may exceed seven feet in height, and are quite imposing to behold. The Ahazu have bright yellow skin, with fiery red markings lining the face and neck and running down the back of the arms, legs and spine. Their features are almost demonic: sloping forehead, forked tongue, thin nostrils, and dark green, pupil-less eyes. The Ahazu converse in shrieks and yells, frequently punctuated by violent gestures and the brandishing of weapons.

A warlike and exceptionally hostile race, the Ahazu make no permanent dwellings, preferring instead to sleep in the treetops. Though slender of build, they are surprisingly strong and agile. Their favored weapons are the gwanga (a heavy, three-bladed throwing knife) and the matsu (a two-handed warclub with a rounded stone head and a long, flexible shaft), both of which they employ with great skill.

The Ahazu will attack without hesitation any creatures who enter their territories. They are fearless in battle, but not to the point of recklessness. If outnumbered, the Ahazu will fall back, attempting to ambush or circle back on pursuing enemy forces. When hunting for food, the Ahazu never venture beyond their own borders. The appearance of a group of Ahazu anywhere outside of the Eastern Junglelands is a certain indicator that they are on the warpath, either launching a raid against the Mud People or tracking a fleeing opponent.

The Imrians never venture into Ahazu land except in heavily armed groups of fifty or more individuals. Rather than engage the Ahazu in battle, the Imrians employ captured bands of Mud People, dire enemies of the Ahazu, as decoys. Once an Ahazu war party has engaged the hapless decoys, the slavers attack, employing throwing nets and vials of toxic powder. Despite the considerable risks entailed in the use of these tactics, the Imrians are persistent in their attempts to acquire Ahazu slaves. Once captured, an Ahazu will never try to escape, the rigid warrior-code of these people prohibiting such practices. For this reason, Ahazu slaves command high prices, and are greatly valued as bodyguards, gladiators, and slave warriors.

Aside from its humanoid population, the Dark Coast is home to many unusual species of plants and animals. The winged ape, a vicious predator capable of gliding from tree to tree, is perhaps the most notorious. It is hunted for its single horn, which is reputed to have potent magical properties. Green and scarlet varieties of lotus grow throughout the region, and are common in the Central Swamplands. The Mud People consider these plants to be delicacies, however, and jealously guard areas where lotus is found in abundance. Amber wasps also proliferate in this region, an indicator that the Swamplands may well be rich in amber nuggets.

Zandir legends associate the Dark Coast region with the Baratus, an ancient race of sea-faring thieves who once roamed the Azure Ocean, preying on merchant vessels and traders. According to the most popular tales, the Baratus buried countless chests of stolen riches in the Eastern Junglelands. Certain Talislantan historians believe that the greater part of this treasure remains mouldering in the ground, awaiting discovery by some fortunate adventurer.

DJAFFA

Surrounded on three sides by the Wilderlands of Zaran, the land of Djaffa consists primarily of scrub plains and desert. With the exception of a few scattered oases, practically nothing grows in this arid region. Djaffa is home to the nomadic peoples known as the Djaffir, who are divided into two tribes: merchant traders and bandits.

By far the most numerous of the two tribes, the Djaffir merchants are generally regarded as the shrewdest and most skillful traders on the continent. Their caravans carry goods to and from the civilized countries of Talislanta, from as far west as Zandu to the eastern lands of Quan and even Xanadas. It is said that the Djaffir merchant tribes will travel anywhere, regardless of the dangers, as long as there is a profit to be made. In truth, the only trails found in certain remote regions are those established over the years by the caravans of these nomadic traders.

The Djaffir bandit tribes, though few in number, are nearly as persistent as their mercantile counterparts. Primarily known as caravan robbers, the bandit tribes are relentless in their pursuit of prey. The larger tribes have been known to raid small villages and settlements, taking women, slaves, and anything of value that can be carried off. Though they will kill in order to get what they desire, Djaffir bandits are not known to engage in wanton or senseless violence. Neither are they known to attack the caravans of Djaffir merchants, a fact which has led many to suspect collusion between the sheiks of the two tribal groups. Some go so far as to cite the distinction between Djaffir merchants and bandits as one of semantics only.

Whatever the relation between the two tribes, it is certain that both have much in common. The Djaffir are uniformly slender and wiry of build, dark-skinned, and of average height. Flowing head dresses, robes, and cloaks of beige or white linen are worn by both tribes, along with boots of soft animal hide. It is the peculiar custom of all Djaffir to wear leather masks, which are made to cover the entire face. The Djaffir will not remove these masks except in the privacy of their tents, believing that "the face mirrors the soul," and that their masks protect them from hostile magics. Fashioned by the Djaffir's wizards, these devices do indeed seem to confer some protection from magical influences, and certainly are of practical use against sand storms (common in Djaffa). Individuals of a more skeptical nature claim that the Djaffir wear masks simply to conceal their identities from those who, by one means or another, they will eventually relieve of their money.

My own experiences with the Djaffir were generally of the most amicable sort, though an acquaintance of mine, the rogue magician Crystabal, claimed to have been less fortunate in his dealings with these people. In one instance, Crystabal sought to outwit a Djaffir merchant, from whom he wished to procure a steed at low cost. After lengthy negotiations, the magician succeeded in acquiring an old but sturdy greymane for the paltry sum of just ten gold lumens; exactly the fee which the Djaffir had quoted as the cost for leasing a steed for a single day.

Convinced that he had gotten the better of the deal, Crystabal rode away in triumph. He awoke on the following day to find the Greymane lying on its back, its four legs thrust skywards in an unmistakable attitude of rigor mortis. The creature's peaceful semblance suggested the cause of death to be old age, leaving Crystabal to ponder the uncanny accuracy with which the Djaffir determined the price of their wares.

The Djaffir produce few marketable wares, though they make lances, daggers and short bows of good quality for their own use. They have some talent for herding and animal husbandry, however, and have managed over time to foster the development of three specialized breeds of Aht-ra, a species of four-legged burden beast: the one-humped Ontra (bred for speed), the two-humped Bactra (bred for speed and strength), and the three-humped Tatra (bred purely for strength and endurance). Generally speaking, the Djaffir bandits prefer the faster one and two-humped beasts, while the merchant traders mainly employ the three-humped Tatra. Other animals herded by the Djaffir include land lizards, greymanes, and the fierce war-beasts known as mangonel lizards.

As the folk of Djaffa are nomads at heart, they have no true cities. The Djaffir do have two settlements, which grow or contract in size according to the comings and goings of the various merchant and bandit tribes. Called El Aran and Al Ashad, both settlements are located at oases; El Aran to the north and Al Ashad to the south. These desert "cities" are comprised entirely of tents and pavilions, allowing them to be moved at need. It is said that the Caliph of Djaffa, whom both the merchants and bandits supposedly regard as their spiritual leader, is always to be found at one of these two settlements. Aside from his duties as arbiter of all tribal disputes, the Caliph of Djaffa performs no other known function. Even so, it is said that at a single word from the Caliph, all the tribes of Djaffa would unite to do his bidding.

FARADUN

Faradun is an exotic land located on the southern coast of Talislanta and bordered to the north by the rugged peaks of the Topaz Mountains. To the east lie two topographical anomalies: the shimmering Sea of Glass and the Emerald Mountain. Arid and hostile terrain dominates the north central region, gradually giving way to patches of jungle along the coast. Blown by winds from the Far Seas, Faradun's climate is uniformly hot and oppressive.

The people who live here, known as the Farad, are a dark and saturnine folk of above average height. They have flint-grey skin, stony visages and narrow eyes as black as coal. The customary mode of dress for Farad males includes elaborate head dress, voluminous robes, broad sashes, and velvet boots, all hung with ornate tassles, fringe, and colored glass beads. Men over the age of twenty wear their beards in twin braids bound with silver fastenings, the length and amount of ornamentation employed being considered signs of status. The Farad women wear long silken gowns, veils, necklaces of silver loops, and rings on each finger. Both the males and females exhibit an air of haughtiness and arrogance that might charitably be described as "distant," or "aloof."

Faradun is perhaps the wealthiest mercantile state on the continent, benefiting from its strategic location as a convenient stop-over point for ships sailing between the Eastern and Western Lands. The sprawling port of Tarun, with its ominous and impregnable defenses, is the capitol and center for all trade in the land. Through the towering sea-gates of Tarun pass the merchant ships of many nations: Imrian slave vessels, Zandir gem dealers, Sunra dragon barques bearing gold and riches from the Quan Empire, Ammanian ore traders, and even Corsair vessels from the Mangar Isles and Gao-Din; the Farad are notable for their singularly unscrupulous business practices, and will buy or sell anything from anyone, with no questions asked.

The societal hierarchy of Faradun reflects the Farad's utter obsession with mercantilism. The ruler of Faradun, called the Cral, wields absolute power, and is responsible for determining market prices for all goods which are to be bought or sold in Tarun. Second in line are the Monopolists, individuals given power by the Cral to determine the availability of the various wares handled by the Farad. Each is responsible for a single commodity, such as slaves, contraband, gemstones, metals, narcotics, and so forth. Some few are wizards, who dabble in magic in order to further their business interests and cartels.

Next come the Usurers, who lend money at exorbitant rates to finance all commercial ventures approved by the Monopolists. Dependent upon the Usurers are the Procurers, who travel far and wide, acquiring merchandise from various sources and establishing new trade contacts. Finally, there are the Mongers: shop-owners, peddlers and hawkers who make up the vast majority of Faradun's citizenry. Few Farad are employed in any non-mercantile line of work. The country's labor force is comprised almost entirely of foreigners, slaves, convicted felons, and burden beasts, while the army and navy are manned by highly paid foreign mercenaries.

The Farad have a religion of sorts, revering the god Avar, deity of material wealth and personal gain. Avar's followers do not erect temples in his name, but prostrate themselves before golden idols purchased in the shops of Tarun. Farad merchants pray to Avar that they might obtain more lucrative contracts than their competitors, and that their profits might increase in proportion to their desires. Deception and treachery are considered astute business tactics, and greed an admirable trait.

Although the Farad are involved to some degree in importing and exporting goods they much prefer to allow such business to come to them. In order to stimulate this type of trade, the Farad make every effort to attract merchants and traders from other lands to the city of Tarun. Prices for food, drink and lodging are quite reasonable, and tariffs and duties are minimal. Further, any sort of entertainment or diversion imaginable can be arranged through the auspices of the Farad Procurers, who claim to be able to grant their customers' fondest desires... for a price. Wealthy foreigners and prospective clients are feted in grand style by the Farad, who can be quite charming when it suits their needs. Conversely, the Farad possess a capacity for cold-blooded, emotionless behavior that is matched only by the barbaric folk of Harak.

My visit to Faradun, while marred to some extent by an unfortunate sea voyage (*Editor's note: See Gao-Din*), was illustrative of the dual nature of the Farad. As is the custom in the port city of Tarun, our ship was hailed before it could enter the harbor, and boarded by grim looking Za mercenaries. All merchandise on board our vessel was examined and inventoried, and each passenger questioned with regard to his or her reason for traveling to Faradun.

Rather than enter into a long and possibly tedious explanation of my own diverse motives, I described myself as a purveyor of rarities and eccentricities; not an entirely inaccurate portrayal, and one which I deemed innocuous enough to avoid attracting undue attention. To my surprise, this statement aroused great interest in the mercenaries. Horns were sounded, and a gold-chased pleasure barge was summoned to take me to shore at once.

The barge docked at a private facility, whereupon I was carried by slave-borne palanquin to an exquisite manse decorated with inlaid mother-of-pearl, cinnabar and jade. Here, I was plied with the costliest wines and delicacies, laved with scented oils and given fresh garments of plush, cinnamon colored velvet. Concubines of heart-rending beauty attended my every need, until at last I was summoned to dine with the owner of the manse. Servants escorted me to a splendid dining hall where for the first time I met my gracious host, a Farad monopolist of regal bearing. It was then that I realized that an error had been made, and that I had been mistaken for some important and long-awaited guest. The hall erupted in a chorus of shouts and accusations, and I took to my heels, escaping only by means of an undignified exit through the sewers of Tarun.

The coastal jungles of Faradun are best avoided, primarily due to the presence of winged apes, death's head vipers, and other unpleasant creatures. Costly k'tallah, tantalus and scarlet lotus grow here in substantial quantities, a fact not lost on the Farad Procurers. Oblivious to the dangers inherent in such work, the Farad send work crews comprised of slaves and convicted felons into the jungles to gather herbs. By careful calculation, the Procurers have determined that the profits realized by harvesting the jungles outweigh the cost in lost slaves by an acceptable margin.

Beyond the edge of the jungle lie lands so arid and barren that not even snakes and vermin dwell there. Ghoulish necrophages, shadow wights, and unclean spirits, being somewhat less particular with regard to their accommodations, haunt the region in force. Called the "Ghostlands" by the Farad, this area has long been used as a place of banishment for those convicted of embezzling funds (a crime considered more heinous than murder in Faradun).

Further east lies the Emerald Mountain, which rises majestically from the center of the Sea of Glass. The so-called "sea" is actually a great expanse of fused green glass. The folk of Cymril pay Faradun a handsome price for the privilege of mining this green crystal, which is utilized extensively in Cymrilian construction. There is always work available here for miners, guards, laborers and caravan drivers, though amenities for such positions are somewhat limited. Windships laden with the finest pieces of green glass disembark from this area once every month or so.

The Emerald Mountain is, much to the Farad's dismay, not truly made of emerald. Neither is it made of green glass, but rather some sort of hard, metallic green ore. The Farad once considered erecting a mining installation at the base of the mountain Kaf, but felt it better not to test the veracity of the old legend, which describes the cloud covered summit of the mountain as being home to the diabolical Shaitan. Adventurers from faraway lands sometimes attempt to scale the Emerald Mountain, seeking the favor of the Shaitan. Never numerous, the ranks of these stalwart heroes seem destined to dwindle further still.

GAO-DIN

P.D. BREEDING © 86

Gao-Din is a small and rocky isle located some ten miles off the western coast of Mog. It is a dismal place, with treacherous swamplands and jungles lining its coastal regions. Inland, limestone cliffs rise up from the murky vegetation, culminating in a great, central mound of stone. Here, looking out across the Azure Ocean, stands the most curious of Talislanta's settlements: the Rogue City of Gao.

Formerly a penal colony of the old Phaedran Empire, Gao was abandoned by its makers during the Cult Wars of the early New Age. The prisoners incarcerated in this heavily fortified installation, mostly thieves and political dissidents, were simply left behind to fend for themselves. Showing a degree of ingenuity born of desperation, the prisoners salvaged an abandoned Phaedran vessel and embarked upon a career as sea-roving pirates. Soon thereafter, Gao-Din was declared an independent city state, and the Rogue City of Gao was made its capitol.

Since that time the Sea-Rogues of Gao have prospered, primarily at the expense of such folk as the Imrian slavers and the Farad. The Sea-Rogues consider themselves to be quite gallant, their swashbuckling antics at the very least setting them apart from the murderous tactics employed by the Mangar Corsairs of the Far Seas. The formal penal colony of Gao has grown into a city of sorts, its old fortifications expanded upon and modified for purposes of defense. The city's current population, comprised mostly of thieves, outcasts and freed slaves, is a remarkable admixture of racial and cultural types: defrocked Ammanian priests, Zandir charlatans, Thrall mercenaries, Green Men, Ahazu, Batrean concubines, and many others.

Rivals and even deadly enemies under normal circumstances, the inhabitants of the Rogue City generally co-exist with a minimum of difficulty on Gao-Din. At least part of the reason for this seems due to the city's unique form of government. The Rogue City of Gao is ruled by an individual known as "the King (or Queen) of Thieves," elected by popular vote once each year. The king's primary duties are to arbitrate disputes, set fair prices for black market and contraband goods, and enforce the three basic tenets of the "thieves' code of honor." Briefly stated, these are: 1) it is illegal to kill a fellow thief (i.e., citizen of Gao) while in the city proper; 2) it is illegal to reveal the seven secret passwords to any non-citizen; 3) it is illegal to steal any item worth more than twenty gold lumens from a fellow thief while in the city proper.

The punishment for failure to comply with the code's tenets is variable, based on the king's appraisal of the exact circumstances surrounding the incident in question. In most cases, however, individuals found guilty of breaking either the first or second tenets are bound, gagged, and fed to the sea demons. Those found guilty of breaking the third tenet are given two weeks to reimburse the victim of the theft three times over. Failure or inability to comply with this edict once again brings the sea demons' alternative to bear.

The Sea-Rogues' system of justice is said to work as well as any other, and bears the distinct advantage of not having to maintain costly facilities for the incarceration of incorrigible felons. An unfortunate side-effect of these policies is that, in order to avoid a high incidence of theft, most of the city's black marketeers and shopowners rarely value any of their wares at less than twenty-one gold lumens. On the plus side, the sea demons who live in the waters around the island are rather fond of the inhabitants of the city, and generally refrain from attacking their vessels. As the Sea-Rogues also feed captured Imrian slavers to the demons, relations between the two races often border on cordiality.

Other strictures governing the citizens of Gao are minimal, most being related to economic or cultural concerns. The government is allowed a ten percent cut of all booty captured by ships which utilize the city's walled-in harbor facilities, but does not otherwise burden the population with taxes or tariffs. While polygamy is permitted by male and female citizens, adultery is frowned upon. Individuals accused of such an indiscretion often simply get married, thereby avoiding possible scandal. As a result of the city's liberal policies concerning marriage, individuals born in Gao may have any number of legal "fathers" and "mothers," and countless relatives of various races and nationalities. Restrictions pertaining to religious beliefs are non-existent, and many diverse cults and religions proliferate in the Rogue City.

Gao citizenship is not easily obtained, though technically available to any thief, outcast, or scoundrel who seeks it. In order to reduce the chance of spies or informants infiltrating Gao's close-knit society, all individuals applying for citizenship must allow themselves to be subjected to scrutiny by the king's personal advisors, a group traditionally comprised of fellow thieves, wizards, astrologers, and the like. Those who pass the test are granted citizenship without further delay, and taught the seven secret passwords required to gain access to the city. Those who fail are seldom heard from again except as regards the sea demons.

Officially, the city state of Gao has no formal relations with any other government, religious group, or secret society. Neither does Gao rule out the possibility of association (usually only on a temporary basis) with almost any government, group, or individual, providing there is a profit to be made by entering into such a relationship. Only the Imrians, Rajans and Ammanians seem exempt from this policy, the Sea-Rogues having a definite aversion to slavers and religious fanatics. Gao-Din extends a degree of professional courtesy to the fierce Mangar Corsairs, which amounts to an agreement that neither will prey on the other's ships. As far as is known, the Sea-Rogues have no contact with the mysterious Black Savants, whose dark vessels occasionally ply the waters of the Azure Ocean.

Forced by circumstances beyond my control (and too convoluted to divulge here) to obtain passage on a Zandir merchant ship, I had a chance to examine the methods of the Sea-Rogues firsthand. We were headed for Faradun, and rounding the southern-most tip of Mog, when the red-sailed Rogue vessel was first sighted. The Zandir captain responded by ordering full sail astern and directing his crew to assume stations suitable for battle. Having no little aversion to sea travel in the first place, I viewed this development with a marked lack of enthusiasm, an attitude which also seemed evident in the faces of most of the crewmen.

Nonetheless, the captain would not be swayed from action. Mounting the ship's forecastle, he struck a defiant pose and called out a challenge to the approaching pirate vessel. In the next instant, he was swept away by an immense stone fired from the Sea-Rogue's ballista; a remarkable shot, actually, considering the distance between the two ships. The first mate, relegated by default to a position of command, ordered a general surrender. The Rogues overtook our vessel and leapt onboard with a great show of flamboyance. Their captain, a gallant fellow attired in dashing cloak and silken hose, politely bade all passengers to divest themselves of their valuables. When all had complied, the Rogues gathered up their spoils and departed, the captain enhancing his exit by means of a low, sweeping bow. This, I realized, was Orianos, whom I had met some weeks earlier in the port city of Zanth.

THE ROGUE CITY OF GAO

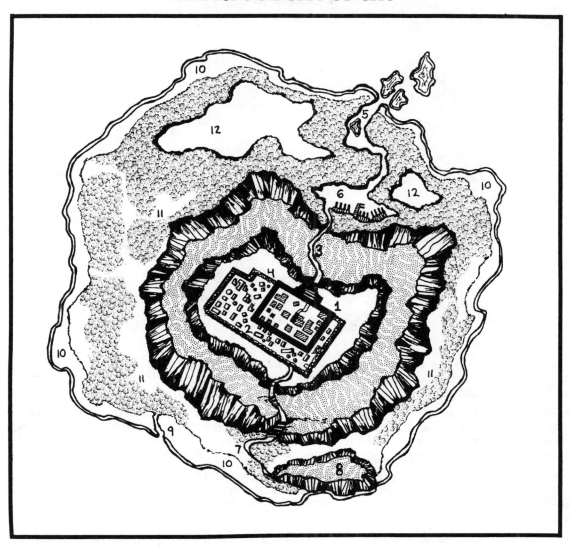

1) Original Structure: Areas shown in black indicate structures built by the Phaedrans. Though much of the old penal colony was torn down by the Sea-Rogues, the prison's outer walls, watchtowers and administrative offices were retained.

2) New City: Following their takeover of the isle, the Sea-Rogues built many new structures, extending the outer walls to encompass a greater area. The new construction varies markedly in quality and architectural style, reflecting the diverse nature of the isle's population.

3) Roadway: The only means of safe access to the city is by this winding road, which was originally built by the Phaedrans. The causeway is wide enough to accommodate a single wagon.

4) Barricade: This is a twenty-foot wall built of cracked stone, dirt and debris. Catapults plundered from sea-going vessels are positioned at strategic points, allowing the city's defenders to rain stones upon would-be invaders entering the harbor below.

5) Inlet: This winding channel leads to the isle's natural harbor. The rock-strewn waters are difficult to navigate, and the channel is vulnerable to attack from defenders commanding the cliffs above. Chains can be drawn across the mouth of the isle at need.

6) Docks: Originally built by the Phaedrans, this facility was modified and expanded by the Sea-Rogues.

7) Deadman's Walk: This is a narrow and very dangerous path which leads to Sea Demon's Point. Criminals facing execution are made to walk this path enroute to their ultimate fate (hence the name, "Deadman's Walk").

8) Sea Demon's Point: From this elevated point convicted felons are tossed to the Sea Demons. A gong is used to notify the demons that a meal is forthcoming.

9) Smugglers' Cove: A small inlet which leads to a subterranean grotto. Supposedly, there is a secret path leading underground to the Rogue City. Sea Demons dwelling beneath the grotto make confirmation of this rumor a low priority for most outsiders.

10) Beach: The scenic white sands which ring the isle seem benign, but are crawling with stinging grey ikshada and other pests.

11) Jungle: The jungles surrounding the isle are infested with biting insects, parasites, poisonous plants, and giant scavenger-leeches.

12) Swamp: As per #11, only worse.

HARAK

Harak is a bleak and desolate land, hemmed in on all sides by mountains and swept by frigid winds from the north. The landscape of Harak is nightmarish: jagged spires of rock jut upwards from the cracked and barren earth, and scattered shards of black iron litter the ground. Here, in this most inhospitable of regions, dwell the fierce warrior clans known as the Harakin.

The Harakin are a hard-hearted people, utterly devoid of mercy or compassion. Ultimate survivalists, they view all other living creatures as prey. Their clans are nomadic, traveling from place to place in search of food and water, both precious commodities in this region. Forced by the circumstances of their existence to endure great hardships, the folk of Harak have no concept of morality or religion, and are by nature fatalistic and grim. They take what they want, raiding neighboring lands and rival clans.

The Harakin are a gray-skinned race, lean and rugged of build and averaging over six feet in height. They dress in loincloths, cowls, high boots, and heavy gloves, usually made of reptile hide. Both the males and females paint the areas around their eyes with black pigments, giving them a fearsome aspect. When their raids have proved fruitless, they subsist on scorpions, snakes, spiders, and bits of lichen and mosses.

Among the folk of Harak, all are considered warriors. Skills and trades not related to warfare are regarded as useless. Each clan member learns to make his or her own weapons, which are hammered and honed from the numerous fragments of black iron found almost everywhere throughout the region. The Harakin employ a number of unique weapons, including the tarak (four-bladed iron axe), khu (double-bladed dagger), krin (a type of heavy crossbow which fires iron spikes) and the jang (a weapon resembling an edged, iron boomerang). All other skills needed to survive (such as hunting, dressing game, finding water, etc.) are considered warriors' skills; the Harakin word for "survival" and "fight" are one and the same.

Although the Harakin show little trace of civilized behavior, they have domesticated the dractyl, a species of winged reptile native to the sheer cliffs of Harak's coastal regions. The Harakin use these creatures for transport and in battle. Though ugly, mean, and ungainly, dractyl require little food and are themselves somewhat edible, factors which hold a certain appeal for their masters. Dractyl are only fair flyers, however, and cannot or will not fly at altitudes in excess of one hundred feet. As a result, the Harakin must often ride them on foot when attempting passage through mountainous regions.

In spite of the shortcomings of their beasts, the warrior clans of Harak are known to range as far as the Quan Empire and the Volcanic Hills in their depredations. They attack nearby L'Haan with lesser frequency, generally considering passage through the towering peaks of Xanadas to be a profitless endeavor. Able to survive the rigors of their own land, the Harakin have little difficulty tolerating the climates and terrains of other regions, most of which seem pleasant by comparison.

An unusual tale regarding these folk is told in Quan. There, it is said, a group of Mandalan scholars once ventured forth on a mission to Harak. By theorizing, they had deduced that the Harakin were not evil beings, but were simply the products of the harsh and cruel environment of their homeland. It was their intention to convince a few of the Harakin to accompany them on the return trip to Quan, where their scholarly theories might be put to the test.

Upon sighting a small band of the nomads, the wise men threw up their hands and raised their voices in greeting. When the Harakin approached, the scholars gave them gifts of gold, fragrant oils, and precious stones. These the Harakin examined, and then discarded. Without apparent enmity they slew the scholars, divested them of their fur cloaks and boots, cut their mounts into sections, loaded everything on their dractyls, and continued on their way.

IMRIA

Imria is a large island located off the southern coast of Mog, in the Azure Ocean. Its dense jungles, twisting inlets and underwater grottoes teem with such dangerous creatures as Kaliya, horned apes, crag spiders, and kra (giant, sightless cave eels). Mt. Talus, a large and intermittently active volcano, rises above the southwestern jungle, and sea demons prowl the coastal waters in force. Perhaps the most dangerous inhabitants of the isle, however, are the amphibious humanoids known as the Imrians.

Tall and muscular, the Imrians have sloping shoulders, scaly yellow-green skin, and dark, deep-set eyes. Their hands and feet are webbed, and their jaws are lined with a double row of sharp teeth. Having both gills and rudimentary lungs, the Imrians are capable of living on land and under the sea. They are powerful swimmers, but are somewhat slow and awkward out of the water.

The Imrians are slavers by trade, preying upon the primitive tribes who dwell along the southern coasts of the Talislantan continent and the Crescent Isles. They are among the only Talislantans who do not fear to sail the open sea. The slavers range far and wide in their massive, barge-like coracles, which are constructed from the bones and hide of kra. Smaller vessels of woven reeds, tethered to the coracles until needed, are used for shore raids and to transport bamboo cages filled with captured slaves. The slavers employ a number of different weapons, including capture-poles, throwing nets, pole hooks, and two rather grisly devices: the oc (barbed bolas) and the korreg (a heavy, two-man crossbow; tri-pod mounted, the korreg works in a way not unlike a harpoon).

The Imrians have but a single settlement, the city of Kragan. Located in a great lagoon situated amidst the central region of Imria, the city consists of hundreds of reed and thatch hovels, each plastered with mud and supported on stilt-like poles. The highest of these structures tower over forty feet above the lagoon, and are occupied by the wealthiest Imrians. Less prosperous Imrians may own hovels which stand just above the water or are partially submerged, according to the tides. Slaves awaiting sale in other lands (and those kept by the Imrians for use as laborers) are generally housed in floating pens moored by heavy lines to the lagoon bottom. The settlement is accessible from the sea by several hidden, winding inlets, each heavily guarded by slave warriors, wild beasts and Imrians.

The Imrians are ruled by a king, who dwells within the highest of Kragan's stilt houses. Among his many responsibilities is the designation of slave shipments to Imria's clients. Quan, Faradun and Zandu vie constantly for Batrean concubines and Sawila courtesans from the Crescent Isles; Amman, Zandu and Quan compete for Green Men from the Dark Coast, whom they employ as gardeners; other clients contend for Mud People laborers, Ahazu warriors, Mogroth swamp-miners, and Chana Witchmen. The Imrians also traffic in narcotic herbs and exotic beasts, which they supply to the merchant-folk of Faradun.

The customs and culture of the Imrians are generally unappreciated by other humanoid races. Most consider the Imrians' taste for slugs, worms and leeches (all Imrian delicacies) disgusting, and find it impossible to enjoy a decent meal in their presence. The light coating of slime which covers the body of a healthy Imrian is likewise unappealing to some, especially clothiers and launderers, who dread the appearance of an Imrian in their establishments. As Imrians drink only brine, their presence in the portside taverns of other lands often portends trouble of one sort or another. The Imrians worship no god, any position bearing greater esteem than "King of Imria" being beyond their comprehension, and mock those who do as ignorant savages.

The Imrians, for their part, consider themselves superior to the other Talislantan races. They claim to be "the first race," from whom the "lesser species" of humanoids are descended. They cite as evidence certain ancient, coral tablets held in their possession for many generations. Retrieved from a sunken crypt by their early ancestors, the Imrians contend that the tablets contain the secret history of their race, dating back over twenty thousand years. Those Talislantan scholars who acknowledge the existence of the Imrian tablets (which are thought to number into the thousands) believe that they do indeed contain priceless information; not of the Imrians, but of some ancient and advanced civilization which sunk beneath the waves untold ages ago.

The magician Crystabal and I suffered an unfortunate encounter with the Imrians following a sojourn to the swamplands of Mog (*Editor's note:* See Mog). The two of us were making for the Jhangaran settlement of Tabal when we were ambushed by a band of thirty Imrians, who emerged from the swamps bearing nets, capture-poles and whips.

With searing spells, Crystabal and I laid low a third of their number. Then the slavers were upon us, frothing at the gills and smelling awfully of brine and decaying vegetation. In short order, we were bound, gagged and thrown into reed boats. The Imrians then conveyed us to their slave coracle, which lay at anchor just off the coast of Jhangara.

Once aboard this vessel, Crystabal and I were shackled with iron fetters and shoved into a large bamboo cage positioned on the ship's deck. The conditions of our interment were abominable: five Green Men, three Jhangaran mercenaries, a pair of squat, six-limbed Mud-People and a great silver-backed mogroth shared our cell, which had been constructed without regard for such considerations as comfort or sanitation. The stench of the Mud-People alone was considerable, to say nothing of the odor emitted by the Imrians and their vessel, which reeked after the manner of rotting fish.

Despite our cramped accommodations, Crystabal and I were able to discern much of what was transpiring about us. Other reed boats continued to arrive, bearing more captives: a dispirited Ahazu warrior, a crew of Jhangaran mud-miners, and a mated pair of winged apes, muzzled and bound with long lengths of heavy chain. Additional bamboo cages were brought forth from below decks, utilizing a crude, winch-and-crane apparatus. The new arrivals were then incarcerated, the winged apes by dint of their ferocity being assigned to a cage separate from the other slaves.

Darkness began to fall, and the Imrians made preparations to depart. A few brought forth lanterns containing scintilla, the luminous eggs of water raknids. Others adjusted the chain harnesses of the three kra employed to tow the slave coracle. One of the Jhangarans was then hauled from an adjacent cage, bound with thongs and lashed to the end of the cable used in conjunction with the Imrians' winch-mechanism. To our horror, the helpless mud-miner was then elevated above the deck, swung to a position some fifteen feet off the ship's prow, and lowered to within inches of the kra's giant, fanged jaws. The blind monstrosities, catching the scent of prey, tugged furiously at their iron chains. Propelled by the activities of the kra, the Imrian coracle pulled out to sea.

To say the least, this situation had done nothing to alter my distaste for waterborne travel. Crystabal, while less prone to hydrophobia, seemed equally pessimistic with regard to our future. Gagged and manacled, there was no way for either of us to effect an escape by the use of our spells. I recalled the sight of the Jhangaran as he dangled in front of the giant kra, and wondered if the Imrians also had some special use for captured wizards and magicians.

My morbid musings were interrupted by a terrible crashing noise, followed by the sound of splintering timbers. The vessel lurched violently to starboard, causing bamboo cages to topple over and sending Imrian sentinels sprawling across the deck. Pulling myself from amidst a tangle of writhing bodies, I saw that we had been rammed by another ship. At the helm of the intruders' vessel, a tall figure in dashing raiment stood, poised in melodramatic fashion: Orianos, captain of the Sea-Rogues of Gao-Din.

For the next few moments, all was chaos. Swinging across on ropes, the Sea-Rogues boarded the coracle, shouting lustily and brandishing their swords and daggers. They were met by the hulking Imrians, who poured forth from below decks armed with flails and barbed spears. The bamboo cage which held Crystabal and the rest of us suddenly burst asunder. The mogroth, aroused to anger by the sudden commotion, had ripped the cage apart with its bare hands. The giant creature waded into the ranks of the Imrians, tossing slavers aside as though they were children.

Crystabal and I ran to the other cages, setting free the rest of the slaves, who fell upon their former captors with great relish. The winged apes somehow won free, and flew off, each bearing a slaver in its talons. Only the Ahazu, bound by the tenets of its warrior code, refused to move from its place of imprisonment. We left the poor fellow behind and entered the fray, hurling caustic spells upon the Imrians.

Within a short time, the battle was over. The Imrians had all been slaughtered, and a number of slaves had perished in the fight. Among the Sea-Rogues, casualties had been slight; Orianos seemed most concerned with his cloak, which had suffered a tear in one spot. Crystabal and I offered to buy him a new one in Zandu, and a barrel of Zandir wine for his crew. With that, we boarded the Sea-Rogues' vessel and set sail for the Western Lands.

JHANGARA

Bordered to the east and west by twin forks of the Axis River, Jhangara is a hot and humid land traveled by few civilized people. Its terrain consists in large part of jungle, murky swamp, and bog, becoming progressively more dense and inhospitable towards the southern coastal regions. Here, untamed marshlands predominate, populated by numerous unfriendly species of animals and plants: kra, winged apes, stranglevine, violet creeper, and the horrid insectoid predators known as water raknids.

The humanoid denizens of this land are the Jhangarans, a backward race, odd and ungainly in appearance. They have marbled brown and sepia-colored skin, elongated limbs, elliptical craniums and pinched, angular features. Both the males and females are hairless, and may attain heights in excess of six and a half feet. The Jhangarans go about bare-footed, wearing only loincloths and bands of coarse cloth wrapped about their arms and legs. The color of cloth employed denotes the individual's status and occupation. Mud-Miners wear grey, Marsh-Hunters wear green, black is for Mercenaries, and red for Outcasts.

The Jhangarans live in tribal groups, typically comprised of individuals of the same occupation. The Mud-Miners and Marsh-Hunters live in rude settlements, the other clans preferring to move from place to place as circumstances dictate. Rivalries between the various tribes are common, the effects of which may range from prejudicial behavior to all-out warfare. There is no love lost between the Mud-Miners and Marsh-Hunters, who have resented each other for centuries. The Mercenaries will fight for anyone who can afford their services, and sometimes attack the other tribes in order to keep in training. A number of the tribes own crude river craft, which they use to ply their various trades along the length of the mighty Axis River.

Strangest of all the tribes are the Outcasts, who wander the swamps and jungles of Jhangara in groups ranging in size from a half dozen to as many as a hundred individuals. Though few in number, the Outcasts wield great power. The other tribes regard them with superstitious dread, and will do almost anything to keep a group of Outcasts from approaching their own camps and settlements. It is the belief of the Jhangarans that all Outcasts bear with them the "stigma of doom." A Jhangaran who is so much as touched by one of "the cursed ones" is immediately branded an Outcast. He or she then has two choices: commit suicide, or join the Outcasts.

In order to avoid being tainted by a tribe of Outcasts, Jhangarans offer them bribes of food, gold or other valuables. These offerings are always placed some distance away from the non-outcasts' encampment or settlement. If the Outcasts find the gifts to be sufficient, they will depart. If not, they may threaten to approach, bearing with them their accursed stigmas. To kill an Outcast, the Jhangarans believe, brings a curse upon the murderer and his or her family. The Jhangarans sometimes try to persuade foreigners to kill Outcasts for them, though few will risk undertaking such grim and dangerous work.

The two largest settlements in Jhangara are Karansk, located to the east, and Tabal to the west. Both are constructed of rude, axe-hewn timbers, and fortified against attack by hostile mercenary tribes, wild beasts and murderous hordes of water raknids. The Jhangarans of Karansk are Mud-Miners, who make their living by dredging amber, gold and sapphires from the surrounding swamps. The Mud-Miners trade with the Ardua of Vardane, receiving various goods from across the Seven Kingdoms.

The Jhangarans of Tabal are Marsh-Hunters, who earn a living by trapping wild beasts and birds (such as the seven-foot tall marsh strider, used as a steed and hunting beast) and hunting for caches of scintilla; silvery globes two to three inches in diameter, which emit a sparkling glow. When removed from the translucent casings which bind them together, scintilla provide a long-lasting and pleasant source of illumination. These unique items are valued at up to one hundred gold lumens apiece, but are unfortunately difficult to come by. Scintilla are actually the eggs of water raknids, which infest the marshlands around Tabal in numbers and bear a distinct hatred for poachers. The Marsh-Hunters trade scintilla, captured beasts, hides, feathers and horn to Zandir freetraders, who travel to Tabal in their coast-hugging merchant vessels.

By and large, the Jhangarans are a sullen and superstitious people, prone to displays of hostile or even violent behavior. They subsist on sea-slugs and raw meat, do not use fire, and have no knowledge of metal-working or magic. Jhangarans have a great weakness for alcohol, and are particularly fond of Zandir wine and chakos, both of which make them mad and unpredictable. The Ardua and Zandir tolerate Jhangaran excesses in order to obtain valuable trade goods, but most other Talislantans deem them untrustworthy. The unscrupulous Farad make no such distinctions, and employ Jhangaran mercenaries as guards and trackers. The Jhangarans, despite their differences, are of one mind concerning the subject of the Septenarial Concordance. This peculiar event occurs once every seven months, when all seven of Talislanta's moons align themselves in the evening sky. The Concordance remains in alignment for fourteen days, during which time no citizen of Jhangara will dare to venture forth into the swamps at night. The Jhangarans claim that the Horag, a monster of immense proportions, stalks the swamplands during the Septenarial Concordance, searching for humanoid victims. Though no Jhangaran has ever claimed to have seen the Horag, their belief in this legendary creature is quite unshakeable; Jhangarans accidentally caught in the swamps after sunset during such times have been known to slit their own throats rather than face the terror of this fearsome monster.

THE JUNGLES OF CHANA

The Jungles of Chana occupy a portion of the southeastern coast of Talislanta, from Faradun to the borders of the Quan Empire. To the west, the jungles meld into rain forest, rising upwards into the Jade Mountains. The climate in this region is hot, wet, and unbearably humid; ideal conditions for Chana's many varieties of tropical plants and trees, which can literally spring up overnight after a drenching rain. Virulent species of animals and insects likewise find the jungles to their liking, making travel in this region a dismal proposition. Worse still are the fierce tribes of savages who dwell here, known collectively as the Chana Witchmen.

The Witchmen are a people of dark and sinister repute, whose tastes for such pastimes as head hunting and cannibalism have endeared them to few other races. A reliance upon various narcotic herbs contributes heavily to the unhealthy appearance of these folk, who are tall and cadaverous in stature, with bilious green skin. The Witchmen do their utmost to appear fearsome, filing their teeth to sharpened points, decorating their glowering visages with occult symbols, and wearing the shrunken heads of their adversaries on cords slung about the neck. It is customary for these folk to wear their hair in a single topknot, lacquered and braided with leather thongs or sinew.

The Witchmen tribes are warlike in the extreme. They fight among each other constantly, each vying for control of the other's territories. They employ throwing sticks, blow-guns, and spears in battle, but generally disdain frontal assaults in favor of ambushes and sneak attacks. In addition to their usual depredations, bands of Witchmen occasionally cross the border into Quan, wreaking havoc on the local villages. Kang troops, stationed at the nearby Quan outpost of Vishana, periodically launch raids into the jungles in retaliation for these assaults. The Kang have a particular loathing for such duty, which they regard as being on a par with hunting for venomous snakes. To instill a more enthusiastic outlook among the troops, Kang commanders frequently offer a bounty of one hundred gold lumens for each Chana head taken on such forays.

The Chana lack any form of civilized virtues, but possess certain undeniably gruesome talents. They are skilled in the concocting of several strange and unique substances, such as devilroot and kesh. The former is an herb poison which can be made to varying toxicity, and may be prepared in powdered or resinous form. Kesh is a pungent liquid derived from the root of the jabutu, a plant found only in the Jade Mountains. It is notable for its profound narcotic and magical properties, and is used extensively in Chana black magic rituals.

The Chana have little talent for domesticating wild beasts, but have learned how to charm the poisonous serpents known as death's head vipers. The Witchmen call these foot-long snakes "wrist vipers," and wear them like deadly, living bracelets. The serpents are trained to attack on command, and have many practical uses.

Perhaps the most infamous of the Witchmen's talents is their reputed ability to steal souls, which they imprison in enchanted stones. These devices, called soulstones, are used to create jujus: mindless zombies controlled through the use of a graven image. Shrunken head fetishes, used to communicate with the lower spirit realms, are also popular. The exact process by which jujus and shrunken head fetishes are made is sufficiently revolting to warrant omission from this text, however.

Chana's jungles are known to harbor an abundance of riches, including costly herbs, precious stones and exotic animals. The Imrians raid the coastal regions on a regular basis, taking Witchmen slaves; there is a market for Chana witch doctors in Faradun, where they are employed in the narcotics and contraband trades. Magical herbs and necromantic paraphenalia are additional lures to the Imrians. Not surprisingly, more than a few Witchmen bear the shrunken and scaly-skinned heads of such souvenir hunters on their belts.

The Jade Mountains of Chana are also rich in natural resources, including black diamonds, moonstones, k'tallah, lotus, devilroot, and a tropical variety of cleric's cowl. The area is populated by winged apes and other terrible creatures, yet is home to one of the most unusual humanoid tribes on the continent, known as the Manra.

The Manra resemble the Witchmen in physical stature, but exhibit none of the frightful or unhealthy characteristics associated with those hostile peoples. They possess the unique ability to assume the forms of other living things, such as wild beasts and even plants. A derivative of the jabutu plant, prepared in some secret manner, is believed to be the source of the Manra's shape-changing abilities. Their tribes are generally peaceful in nature, though deviant Manra clans are known to exist. Both types bear considerable resentment for the Witchmen tribes, their rivals for the region's limited supply of jabutu plant.

While traveling at the behest of the Emperor of Quan (*Editor's note: See Quan*), I once made the grievous error of venturing too near the territories of the Chana Witchmen, a misstep which nearly brought a premature ending to my career. With me at the time were a contingent of crimson-skinned Kang warriors and Zen, a beautiful Mandalan Savant enslaved by the Quan and assigned to guide our party. I had just finished compiling a series of notes on the jabutu plant when several of the Kang's great, lizard-like striders suddenly became irritable, clawing the ground and emitting loud, squawking sounds. The Kang, perplexed by the behavior of their mounts, sought to quiet the beasts, without success.

Not a moment later, the source of the striders' agitation became all too apparent. From the edge of the jungle a howling band of Witchmen sprang forth, forty strong and armed with spears and blowguns. Poison darts buzzed like angry wasps among us, felling warriors and striders alike. Though the Kang fought with their usual ferocity, our attackers enjoyed the twin advantages of surprise and superior numbers. They quickly overran our position, a blow to the head rendering me unconscious while the battle still raged.

I awoke suspended by ropes above a great cauldron of roiling liquid, which filled the air about me with acrid vapors. A cursory glance from side to side put my situation in perspective: darkness hung over the jungle, the only source of illumination being the flames which stoked the cauldron beneath my feet. Seated around the fire, an entire tribe of Witchmen watched with grim fascination as two of their number prepared to lower me into the vat.

Suddenly, a spectral form stepped forward from the darkness, its body emitting a weird incandescence. The Witchmen were at once seized with fear, and fled in mindless terror into the depths of the jungle. The phantasm turned towards me and, to my surprise, uttered a laugh; it was Zen, my Mandalan guide. Anticipating the result of our battle with the Witchmen, she had hidden in the jungle, and so eluded capture. When she saw that I had been taken alive, Zen followed at a safe distance and waited for nightfall. She then rubbed her face, hands and garments with a type of phosphorescent fungi native to the region. This gave her the semblance of a radiant spirit-form, an appearance which Zen believed would frighten the Witchmen, who have a superstitious dread of benevolent spirits.

Without further delay, Zen freed me from my bonds and lowered me to the ground. No longer under the supervision of the Kang guards, we elected to head west towards Carantheum, where Zen would no longer be a slave to the Quan Empire.

KHAZAD

Khazad is a strange and largely unknown realm located at the furthest north western reaches of Talislanta. Practically inaccessible to all but the most determined and knowledgeable travelers, its terrain is quite foreboding. A line of precipitous cliffs runs the length of its western coast, and a ridge of mountains extends along its eastern borders. To the north lie fields of ice and snow; beyond this is the Midnight Sea, where sailors fear to go. The waters of the Gulf of Silvanus, rock-strewn and perilous, deny easy access from the southeast.

As a result of these impediments to travel, much of what is known of Khazad is based upon the accounts of the wandering Sarista tribes and the few hardy adventurers who have risked journeying to this isolated area. According to their accounts, the interior of Khazad is less than inviting. Patches of bleached and barren gall oak stand like skeletons, silhouetted against a dreary, purple and grey sky. Broken and irregular lines of hills dot the landscape, interspersed with moors, quagmires, and stagnant ponds. The air is heavy with the smell of moldering vegetation, and exudes an unsettling, ancient quality.

Scattered throughout the country are ruins, evidently of some long-forgotten civilization. Though a few have been plundered of their hidden secrets, others remain largely unexplored. Far to the north are vast burial grounds, denoted by row upon row of age-worn stone markers. Less frequently encountered are mausoleums of pitted stone, engraved with arcane symbols of obscure origin. Humanoid remains, entombed in massive sarcophagi of strange design, have been found in some of these crypts. Apparently individuals of some importance, these men and women of Khazad were buried wearing gold funerary masks of frightening aspect. In the less elaborate tombs and graves, similar masks of silver, copper, tin, and lead have been unearthed. Though the purpose of these artifacts is unclear, some scholars believe the masks were intended to ward demons or evil spirits from the bodies of the deceased. The value of the metal used in the making of these masks is believed to have been a measure of the wearer's social status or rank.

Also favored are the brass urns found in the tombs of this region. Sealed with paraffin, these devices were used to imprison bottle-imps, and to safekeep the corpse-dust of departed wizards. Prized by curio collectors and Necromancers alike, these relics bring high prices in some places. Accordingly, the Sarista occasionally venture into Khazad for the express purpose of acquiring such artifacts. The risks entailed in this practice are not inconsiderable. Necrophages haunt the region, craving fresh corpses in preference to the dry bones of the Khazad dead. Lurkers prowl the moors, as do packs of tundra beasts from the Serpentine Mountains. Wind Demons, though far from common in Khazad, are sometimes known to leave their larva in the hollows of the dead gall oaks found in this area.

There is a legend to the effect that a vast complex of ruins lies far to the north. Referred to as Necron on many ancient maps, the Sarista call it the "City of the Dead." Here, it is believed, are buried the mummified remains of an entire city's population. The Sarista claim that the city is cursed, and say that it is death to enter it. Others believe that the Sarista tell such tales to frighten away would-be grave robbers from their own private plundering grounds.

The magician Crystabal and I were intent on finding this lost city, and so made preparations to travel to Khazad. Our plans were hampered when it became apparent that we could find no Zandir or Sarista guide willing to undertake such a mission. Fearing that further delay would force postponement of the trip due to the spring rains, we decided to go it alone. We purchased the necessary supplies in the Zandir capitol of Zanth and were on our way.

All went reasonably well until we reached the northern borders of Silvanus. Here, we had thought to forge the Necros River and follow an old Sarista trail into the Serpentine Mountains. An early thaw unexpectedly caused the river to overflow its banks, necessitating a change in strategy. We headed south, hoping to cross the Necros by means of a rope and wood slat bridge notated on Crystabal's map. Along the way, we were attacked by an exomorph. Crystabal dispatched the monster with a Spell of Elemental Fire, but not before one of our steeds had been slain.

At this point, I suggested that we temporarily abandon the quest and return to Zandu. Crystabal, an adventurous and hot-headed youth, would hear none of it. We finally reached the bridge, only to find that it had been washed out. Stopping to make camp and discuss our situation, I discovered that a band of mischievous woodwhisps had absconded with the remainder of our food. Crystabal and I exchanged meaningful glances, then packed up our gear and rode off in the direction of Zandu. A heavy rain commenced, signaling the premature onset of spring.

L'HAAN

L'Haan is a land of vast snow fields, glittering ice peaks, and frozen lakes. Located in the nethermost reaches of eastern Talislanta, the region is predominantly wilderness, populated by tundra beasts and great herds of Snowmane and wooly ogriphant. Along the shores of the Sea of Ice live the only civilized folk native to L'Haan: the blue-skinned humanoids known as the Mirin.

The Mirin are a noble race, tall and statuesque in appearance. They live in crystalline ice castles, and are skilled in the arts of enchantment, alchemy, and elemental magic. Renowned throughout Talislanta as artificers of the highest order, the Mirin fashion superior weapons and implements of adamant, an alloy of silver and blue diamond, the fabled "permanent ice" of legend; actually, a lustrous gemstone possessing significant magical properties.

There are two large Mirin settlements in L'Haan: the twin cities of Rhin and L'Lal, situated on opposite shores of the Sea of Ice. L'Lal, located closest to the territories of the evil Ice Giants of Narandu, is surrounded by walls over forty feet in height. Rhin is the capitol of L'Haan, and it is here that the ruler of the Mirin, known as the Snow Queen, resides. A figure of some mystery to outsiders, the Snow Queen is said to be a white witch of surpassing ability. Travel between the two cities is mainly by ice schooner, majestic sail-driven vessels which glide across the Sea of Ice on runners made of gleaming adamant.

The Mirin army, much-hardened by long campaigns against the Ice Giants of Narandu, the Harakin, and the Frost Demons of the Opal Mountains, is considered by some to be the finest fighting force on the continent. Equipped with light chain mail, swords, shields, and spears of adamant, the Mirin present a formidable challenge to intruders venturing into their territories. Mirin war sleds, drawn by teams of Snowmanes, allow swift response to threats from all across the realm.

A deeply religious people, the Mirin revere Borean, God of the cold North Wind. The white witches and warlocks of Borean do not build temples in his name, but erect altars on the snowy steppes around L'Lal and Rhin. It is only in such open and natural surroundings, they say, that one can feel the true presence of the God of the North Wind.

The Mirin rarely venture beyond their own borders, as they are incapable of tolerating any but the coldest climes. Druas from the Maze-City of Altan sometimes come here, as does at least one tribe of hardy and extremely determined Djaffir merchants. Despite generous offers from many foreign lands, the Mirin refuse to trade any but the smallest quantities of blue diamond or adamant, substances which they consider vital to the defense of their land.

Nevertheless, adventurers and fortune seekers have long risked the perils of the Opal Mountains in the hope of finding deposits of blue diamond. The most common route, through the Volcanic Hills and the Valley of Mist, is recommended only to those whose sense of adventure is matched by equal measures of courage and/or insensate recklessness. Saurans and raknids, a hideous cross-breed of scorpion and demon, roam the Volcanic Hills, while vorls (vile creatures composed of insubstantial vapor) haunt the Valley of Mist. Those fortunate enough to reach the Opal Mountains may expect to be accosted by Frost Demons, who are attracted by the body heat given off by warm-blooded creatures.

The Druas known to me as Shadowmoon (*Editor's note: See Tamaranth*) was a friend of the blue-skinned Mirin. By means of a trail known only to his people, we journeyed to L'Haan; I, hoping to acquire a small quantity of blue diamond, and he in response to some inner voice, the nature or intent of which Shadowmoon did not deign to discuss.

Taking care to avoid the less-friendly denizens of this frozen land, we rode on swift snowmanes towards the Ice City of L'Lal. Shadowmoon spoke not a word throughout the course of our trip, which was not unusual for one of his race, though I felt that the quality of his silence now bore some additional meaning. Several miles from L'Lal we were met by a platoon of twenty Mirin scouts clad in gleaming adamant, whose duty it was to patrol the perimeters of the Crystal City. Here, Shadowmoon learned that Ardan, a Mirin to whom he had been bound in friendship had died of wounds sustained in battle with the Ice Giants of Narandu.

Without show of outward emotion, the Druas accompanied the scouts to the gravesite of his friend, who had been interred beneath the frozen tundra. He stood there in silence while I went on to L'Lal, where I carried out my business with a heavy heart, trading six fine moonstones for a single, flawless blue diamond. On the following day I returned to find Shadowmoon as I had left him, still maintaining his lonely vigil. After a time, the Druas sat astride his snowmane, and we departed.

MOG

Mog is a vast swampland cut by countless small tributaries of the Axis River. Travel on foot through this region is quite impractical, and recommended only to those who possess an unreasoning fondness for wading in knee-deep, murky waters. Explorers who venture into this realm generally do so in flat-bottomed boats, the gnarly roots of giant bombo trees serving as suitable anchorage for this type of craft.

The swamps of Mog teem with a variety of unusual plant and animal species. Morphius, a parasitic plant whose blossoms emit a sleep-inducing fragrance, grows among the branches of certain trees, as does serpentvine, an obnoxious, biting species of plant which subsists on small birds and reptiles. Deadman, a plant whose pale, white leaves exude a deadly contact poison, is of use in deterring woodwhisps and flits, both of which are a great nuisance to travelers. K'tallah plant and black lotus, two herbs which possess extreme hallucinogenic and mind-altering properties, are highly sought after by dealers of contraband goods. The region's primary resource is amber, however, which is a lure to freetraders, prospectors and opportunists from across the Western Lands and the Seven Kingdoms.

Of intelligent species native to this region, the Mogroth are most common. Huge, sloth-like humanoids, the Mogroth live in rude huts erected in the branches of large mung-berry trees. They subsist on the leaves and fruit of these trees, which are remarkably bitter, and shunned by other creatures. The Mogroth, on the other hand, claim that only those of refined tastes are capable of appreciating the mung's distinct savor. Though they are notoriously lazy and slow-moving, Mogroth occasionally dredge the swamps for bits of gold and amber, both of which are found here in some quantities. These they trade to foreigners in return for strong drink, which they favor greatly. The more ambitious of these creatures will sometimes travel to Jhangara or the Seven Kingdoms, bearing sacks of gold and amber. Being somewhat dull-witted, the Mogroth seldom strike a hard bargain for their wares, a fact which draws unscrupulous and conniving merchants to them like flies to honey.

By far the most unusual creature to inhabit the swamps of Mog is the rare and exotic gold beetle. These strange insects, which may measure from up to four inches in length, feed on tiny bits of gold washed down the tributaries of the Axis River. In time, their wings and carapaces begin to take on a golden lustre. By adulthood, the beetle's entire body is fully transmuted to gold of the purest sort.

Gold beetles are highly treasured as pets by wealthy Zandir, Thaecians, and especially the Quan. Fine specimens may bring as much as two thousand gold lumens each, such is their rare beauty. Gold beetles are fragile creatures, however, and must be handled with extreme care. Dead, they are worth no more than a few silver pieces. These rare insects are solitary in nature, and tend to nest amidst such noxious plants as deadman and morphius, neither of which have any effect on gold beetles.

The Amber Wasp, a pestiferous version of the gold beetle, also inhabits the swamplands of Mog. As its sting is quite painful, it is understandably sought after with considerably less vigor than its more benign counterpart. Of interest to adventurers will be the news that giant leeches, cave bats, and lurkers (swamp demons) are also found here.

In all candor, slogging through the swamps of Mog had not been high on my list of priorities until I visited Cymril, capitol of the Seven Kingdoms. There, a Kasmir money lender offered me a sizeable sum of gold to travel to Mog and return with a shipment of costly herbs. My initial reaction was one of disinterest. A severe shortage of funds caused me to reconsider, however, and I accepted the assignment.

My first step in preparing for the journey was to hire a mercenary Thrall to act as guide. I would advise any considering a trip to Mog to do the same. While these muscular and war-loving folk have little skill at woodlore, they know well the swamps of this region and are handy with a blade. Also with us was Crystabal, a young magician whom I'd met while in Cymril.

We took one of the seven roads from Cymril to Taz, then followed a series of trails through the jungle. Fording the Axis River, we entered Mog. Our Thrall guide, who called himself Ramm, proved invaluable, particularly during a brief but harrowing encounter with a tentacled lurker. About five miles into the swamp, we met up with a group of three Mogroth. None of us could believe the size and bulk of these creatures, who dwarfed even the mighty Ramm. As our employer had instructed us, we gave the Mogroth twelve casks of Arimite liquor. In return, they handed over to us a quantity of black lotus, tantalus and k'tallah worth twenty times what we had given them. Crystabal and I rued the inequity of this exchange, which we felt took unfair advantage of the Mogroth. We paid the Mogroth each an additional sum of gold and headed instead towards Jhangara, leaving the Kasmir to ponder the wages of sin.

NARANDU

P. D. BREEDING © 86

Narandu is an immense and frozen wasteland which stretches across much of the far northern regions of Talislanta. Here, jagged mountains of ice pierce the bleak tundra, and frigid winds howl through chasms ringed with hoarfrost. Only the hardiest creatures can survive in this torturous region, which is home to the monstrous beings known as the Ice Giants.

These creatures are aptly named indeed, for their bodies are composed entirely of solid ice. They are frightening to behold, standing well over ten feet in height and weighing as much as one ton. Spiky protrusions of ice cover their bodies, and their hands and feet are clawed. Although they are bestial and lack great intelligence, the Ice Giants are formidable foes. Their very bodies emanate a piercing cold, so much so that large groups of Ice Giants can effectively lower temperatures in a wide-radius area.

By advancing further and further south each year the Ice Giants have slowly extended their territories, converting temperate lands to bleak tundra by establishing settlements in these areas. The avian Gryphs of Tamaranth have long warned of these intrusions, though generally to little avail. Even scholars who acknowledge the veracity of the Gryphs' claims contend that the Ice Giants' southern progress is so gradual as to warrant little concern; most estimate the rate of advancement at less than one half foot per year. Despite the fact that the Ice Giants advance along nearly a thousand mile front, these scholars claim that the loss of land in real terms is so minimal as to be insignificant.

The Ice Giants are ruled by a mysterious being known only as the Ice King. Unlike his brutish subjects, who know nothing of magic, the Ice King is a powerful warlock. His sworn enemy is the Snow Queen of L'Haan, who has long opposed the Ice King's plans of conquest. Fierce battles, pitting the Ice King's legions against the Snow Queen's armies of Mirin, have raged along the borders of L'Haan for many centuries.

The land of Narandu is rich in deposits of blue diamond, the magical substance known as "permanent ice." The Ice Giants lack the knowledge of how to utilize the magical properties of these gemstones, but mine them nonetheless for use in making crude weapons. War clubs embedded with uncut blue diamonds are used in battle to some effect by many of the Ice Giants.

The Ice Giants do not erect permanent structures of any kind, though they are known to carve tunnels and caverns in the sides of glaciers or mountains of ice. In these places are stored blue diamonds, articles obtained in battle with the Mirin, and the frozen carcasses of such creatures as muskronts, tundra beast and wooley ogriphant (Ice Giants cannot obtain nourishment from anything that is not frozen solid). The Ice King is said to dwell in a massive mountain complex of similar design, though its location remains unknown.

Aside from its giant population, Narandu is also home to man-eating frostweres and the fearsome creatures known as Frost Demons. Both subsist on warm-blooded prey, and in fact are not totally unalike in appearance. Although frost demons are winged, this distinguishing feature is often difficult to note, as these creatures have the habit of folding their wings and traveling on foot. It is believed that their eyesight is poor, and that frost demons engage in this practice when tracking prey. A certain way of telling the two creatures apart is to examine the eyes: Frostweres have pupil-less grey orbs, while those of the Frost Demon are more violet in color.

The harsh climate of Narandu allows few plants to prosper in these territories. The exception is the silvery-white snow lilly, a plant which, when prepared in an elixir or potion, has the virtue of conferring resistance to cold. As one can only find this plant by traveling to frigid Narandu, the purpose of obtaining snow lilly might seem somewhat irrational to those of skeptical or pessimistic bent.

One of the more unusual features of this region is the great chasm known as the Black Pit of Narandu. Located just north of Tamaranth, this supposedly bottomless fissure is the source of many colorful legends. Some claim the Black Pit leads to the demon-haunted dimension of Cthonia. Others believe the Pit to be the entrance to an extensive system of tunnels which wind their way as far south as the Wilderlands of Zaran. Certain scholars, noting the clouds of steam which issue from its gaping mouth, theorize that the Black Pit exits into a vast, underground sea. Even less likely explanations of this geographical phenomenon exist, none of which the author will dignify by mentioning them within the pages of this tome.

During the time I spent exploring the continent of Talislanta, I never once felt even the slightest urging to venture within sight of this frigid and foreboding realm. Being a firm believer in reincarnation, the Druas known as Shadowmoon was perhaps less protective of his current physical manifestation than I, and so had visited Narandu numerous times. He described to me those shimmering ice peaks, streaked with brilliant red and gold in the light of Talislanta's setting suns. When this instilled no trace of wanderlust in me, he talked of blue diamonds, each the size of a man's fist and sparkling with a frozen azure fire.

Perhaps it was the manner in which his people speak, which conveys in a few words a multitude of thoughts and images. Perhaps it was the fact that my financial resources had once again been eroded by the demands of travel. Whatever the reason, the following dawn found the two of us bound for the frozen wastes of Narandu.

All was indeed as Shadowmoon had described, though I might have appreciated a more accurate account of the prevailing climate, which exceeded my previous conception of the term, "freezing cold." After a time, we came upon an irregular mountain of ice, about which was scattered a profusion of huge, four-clawed tracks. Shadowmoon dismounted and followed the tracks, which led to a cavernous opening in the side of the glacier. Charging me to watch over our steeds, the Druas calmly went forth into the cave.

I stood listening near the mouth of the cavern, but if any sounds emanated from within they were lost in the howling of the northern winds. It began to snow, and then an icy hail rained down upon the bleak terrain. An indefinite amount of time passed, during which I was forced to consider the prospect that my companion had met some untimely demise. I questioned the wisdom of maintaining my vigil, but could not leave the Druas behind.

My perseverance was finally rewarded when Shadowmoon appeared at the cave entrance, bearing with him a small sack of rude cloth. He appeared in good health, a few superficial wounds and rents in his garments notwithstanding. "The Ice Giant Yldre, who brought death to Ardan of L'Haan, has been sent to his next incarnation," said the Druas. Handing me the sack, which contained a number of uncut blue diamonds, Shadowmoon bade us depart the land of Narandu. It was my pleasure to comply, and at once.

NEFARATUS

P.D. BREEDING © 86

Rising ominously above the waters of the Far Seas is the Isle of Nefaratus, a shadowy mound of black ironrock rimmed with jungle. Bleak towers of stone dot the isle, each a hundred feet in height and decorated with the graven images of leering devils. Within, the inhabitants of Nefaratus gaze into mirrors of polished obsidian, and work their dire enchantments and divinations. These are the Black Savants, members of a secret magical order that dates back to the Forgotten Age.

The Black Savants are scholars of the occult, whose interests range from diabolism to all aspects of the lower planes. They stand nearly seven feet in height, and are stoop-shouldered and gaunt in appearance. The traditional costume of the Black Savants includes boots, gloves, cloak and robes of satiny black cloth, hooded and veiled so as to obscure their features. Only their eyes are normally visible; cold, unfeeling orbs like twin shards of onyx. They carry staves and blades made of black adamant, a rare alloy of silver and black diamond. Only the Black Savants know how to make this metal, which has potent magical properties.

The precise motives of these mysterious beings have long been subject to speculation. Their midnight-black vessels are rumored to sail the cursed waters which lie at the edge of the world. Sailors who have encountered such vessels at sea claim that they are propelled by the efforts of demons, chained to the oars with silver shackles and driven on by giant, copper-skinned devils. Others claim to have seen the black ships pull into certain port cities on moonless nights, only to depart before the coming of dawn.

The Black Savants rarely associate with other peoples, a situation which most decent folk find quite acceptable. Some few have been known to serve as the advisors of kings and tyrants, though seldom for any great length of time. As they do not generally allow ships within their territorial waters, practically nothing is known of their homeland. The Imrian slavers have an arrangement with the Black Savants, by which— in return for slaves and other unknown considerations—they are allowed to pass through Nefaratan waters by certain, prescribed routes. It is not known whether the Imrians deal with the Black Savants by choice, or because they fear to do otherwise.

Korak, greatest sorcerer of ancient times, wrote of the Black Savants in Volume Nine of his renowned "Guide to the Lower Planes." In it, he states: "The Black Savants of Nefaratus are adept in the lore of the dark dimensions, and possess certain knowledge of these regions, particularly the Lower Plane of Oblivion. They employ enchanted devices known as obsidian mirrors, which function as viewports and gateways into the nether realms."

"In order to facilitate my own research on the lower planes, I sought to obtain one of these useful items from the Black Savants. This I managed to do, but at such a price as to nearly ruin me. Fortunately, I managed to convince one of their number to accept a pair of earth demons, imprisoned in vats of saline solution, in exchange for one third of the stated price. The remainder of the fee I was required to pay in silver, as the Black Savant would not accept gold. What became of the earth demons, I do not know; one can assume their fate to have been unpleasant, for the Black Savants are diabolists, who despise all demons as much as their mentors, the Shaitan, do."

OCEANUS

As any reader of these accounts will surely know, the thought of sailing across vast stretches of treacherous waters, in order to arrive at a city which floats upon the waves, held no appeal whatever for the author. Thus, what follows is a rendering of certain facts related to me by the Sea-Rogue Orianos whom I had the relative good fortune of meeting while in the port city of Zanth, among other occasions.

Oceanus is a waterborne city established some centuries ago by wandering tribes of Sea Nomads. Built entirely upon great barges made of plant fibers and tethered to each other in intricate fashion, the city has no permanent location. Though apparatus allowing the city to be moored to the sea-bottom can be employed as desired, Oceanus is most often allowed to float freely on the waves. Besides increasing the productivity of Oceanus' food-gatherers (fishermen and kelp farmers), this practice effectively disguises the city's location, and acts as a deterrent against roving Corsair bands.

The Sea Nomads who built Oceanus are a green-skinned, dark-haired folk of average height and slender build. Their style of dress is best described as eccentric: vests of irridescent scales, loin cloths of rainbow kra's hide, and necklaces of colorful shells being most popular. Their warriors augment this basic wardrobe with shields of zaratan tortoise shell and fierce-looking helms made from the skulls of Sea Demons. The most commonly employed weapons are swords fashioned from the bones of rainbow kra, barbed spears, and a peculiar type of light crossbow that unleashes a half-dozen sea anemone spines with a single shot (called the flange-bow).

The customs and culture of the Sea Nomads of Oceanus are similarly unique, and perhaps even bizarre. According to their historians (who, despite the seeming limitations of the form, relate their tales via the use of pantomime), the Sea Nomads once dwelled in a far-off land. When a natural disaster of cataclysmic proportion caused their homeland to sink beneath the waves, the inhabitants fled in boats. In their haste, or so the historians claim, the escapees left behind a certain hag named Jezem, noted as a practitioner of black magic. Out of spite Jezem placed a murrain upon her people prior to her demise, that they might never again dwell upon the land without invoking consequences of the most dire sort.

Though the nature of these consequences was never specified, the survivors thought it best not to tempt fate by testing the efficacy of the hag's magics. Accordingly, they became nomadic seafarers. At some later date the Sea Nomads built Oceanus, deeming this to be a most clever way of foiling the hag's curse. To the present day, however, no Sea Nomad will set foot on land, believing that to do so would bring down some nameless doom upon themselves.

CITY OF OCEANUS

The floating city of Oceanus stands as perhaps the ultimate testament to Talislantan man's defiance of nature (or of common sense, depending upon one's point of view). Construction of the settlement, begun some three hundred years ago, remains an ongoing process; both to accommodate a growing population and due to the ravages of wind, water and sea dragons.

The Sea Nomads have learned how to utilize the ocean's natural resources to fit their needs. Materials used in construction include coral, sponges, the hide and bones of sea dragons and other aquatic creatures, and adhesives derived from the secretions of various species of shellfish. The primary source of building materials, however, is yellow aqueor, a giant species of kelp which can grow to lengths of up to five hundred feet. The plant's massive trunk, cut into sections and dried by exposure to sunlight, takes on a buoyancy and tensile strength similar to wood. The leaves are edible, and the fibrous stems can be used to make rope, parchment, mats, baskets, and even a type of coarse cloth. All the products derived from the yellow aqueor are remarkably resistant to rotting and water-logging.

Some of the many unusual features of the floating city include:

1) Sails: Though incapable of swift or precise movement, Oceanus is capable of movement through the water, and can be "steered" along a designated course. A great profusion of sails, masts and riggings is employed to give the city impetus.

2) Barge-Platforms: These floating platforms serve as the city's foundation. They are made of "timber" from the yellow aqueor, lashed together by means of an intricate network of ropes.

3) Rudder: The shoulder-blade of an ancient sea dragon has been employed to this purpose for many generations.

4) Anchor Lines: These lines allow the floating city to be anchored to the ocean bottom as needed.

5) Dwellings: The Sea Nomads live in stilt-dwellings built of yellow aqueor "timber" and "thatch." Rope ladders afford entry into the upper levels.

6) Zaratan Pens: These partially-submerged enclosures serve as stables for the colony's Zaratan.

7) Defensive Fortifications: Positioned at various points around the perimeter of the city, each of these towers is equipped with a massive ballista made of sea dragon horn and bone. These devices employ two types of ammunition: giant, flaming "javelins" and massive harpoons (used vs sea dragons and other aquatic monsters).

PHANTAS

Phantas is a semi-tropical isle, covered in vegetation and surmounted on all sides by wavering cliffs of white stone. The isle is home to an uncountable number of weird plants, animals, and beasts, many of which are to be found nowhere else in Talislanta. High above the island, tethered to the ground by chains of adamant, is a singular structure: a great castle built in the clouds, called Cabal Magicus. Here dwell the last descendants of an ancient race of magicians and thaumaturges, known as the Phantasians.

A pale-skinned people, the Phantasians are tall and very thin, with delicate features reminiscent in some ways of the Thaecians. They dress in long, trailing robes, conical caps, and necklaces of colored crystals. Once among the most skilled practitioners of the magical arts, the Phantasians have forgotten nearly all of the fabled knowledge possessed by their ancestors, who built Cabal Magicus and fostered many of the strange and unusual plant and animal species which populate the island. Among the few secrets left to them are the talents associated with the building of windships and the art of distilling dream essence. It is the latter ability which provides the Phantasians with their livelihood, such as it is. By means of a complex series of undertakings the Phantasians are able to capture the stuff of which dreams are made, and contain the distilled fluid dream essence in amberglass vials. These the Phantasian dream merchants pack in velvet-lined chests and transport by windship to such places as Cymril of the Seven Kingdoms, Thaecia, Zandu, Faradun and the Quan Empire.

As dream essence can cost as much as nine hundred gold lumens per dram, only the wealthiest of individuals can afford to partake of this exotic substance. Many consider dream essence to be an over-priced and frivolous item, having no practical use whatever. As such, the Phantasian dream merchants seldom turn a profit on their wares. Most of their earnings are used just to keep Cabal Magicus afloat, maintain their windships, and feed their families. Nonetheless, they continue on, resolute in the pursuit of their dreams.

The Isle of Phantas is seldom visited by other peoples, its rather isolated location serving as a deterrent to all but the most determined voyagers. The Imrians once invaded Phantas, but fled upon encountering certain of the isle's more bestial inhabitants. The astounding array of flora and fauna unique to Phantas does occasionally lure a few dedicated scholars and naturalists to the island, who must usually suffer the company of adventurers in order to make safe their journey to this faraway place.

Having left the Farad city of Tarun in some haste (*Editor's note: See Faradun*), I was fortunate enough to meet up with a Phantasian dream merchant whose windship had broken down along the coast of Faradun. In return for my assistance in repairing the ship's damaged levitationals, the Phantasian agreed to transport me to Zanth, capitol of Zandu. The two of us effected the necessary repairs in short order, and took to the air.

Enroute, the Phantasian and I discussed our respective situations over a bottle or two of Zandir wine. He professed to have become tired of the business of selling dream essence, and took to drinking heavily. It soon became apparent that my host had lost all semblance of sobriety: singing loudly and off-key, he reeled across the ship's deck, arms akimbo and head thrown back in a crude version of the Caperetto, a popular dance of the day.

Just then the windship hit a sudden downdraft, causing the vessel to lurch precariously to portside. I grabbed the ship's rail barely in time to avoid being thrown overboard, but the Phantasian was not so fortunate. Wine bottle still in hand, he plunged into the sea and was never heard from again. With a heavy heart I took command of the windship and its contents, and once again set sail for Zanth.

THE PLAINS OF GOLARIN

East beyond the Darklands of Urag lie the grassy steppes of the Plains of Golarin. It is a place of some mystery; the crumbling ruins of an unknown number of ancient civilizations litter parts of the interior, long abandoned by their makers and overgrown with weeds and creepers. In the north central region stands the Watchstone, an immense pillar of grey basalt several miles in height. An age-worn stairway, carved into the face of the Watchstone, winds upward in a slow, twisting spiral. From the summit, it is said, one can see clear across Golarin. Where once mighty armies clashed on the plains of battle, now roam great herds of greymanes, ogriphant, and giant, six-legged megalodonts. What lost secrets lay hidden here remain largely a matter of speculation, this due in great part to the nature of Golarin's current occupants: the predatory Beastmen.

The Beastmen of Golarin are savage beings, ignorant and primitive, yet possessed of a certain animalistic cunning. A coat of bristling fur covers their muscular frames, usually dirty brown or grey in color. Though humanoid in form, their features are reminiscent of wild beasts: slavering fangs, deep-set eyes, pointed ears and protruding jaws typify the vast majority of these folk.

The Beastmen exhibit few civilized traits, though they are able to employ the fierce steeds known as darkmanes. The more intelligent members of their species sometimes set crude traps designed to disable prey. Having no noticeable talent as craftsmen, their weaponry and equipment is limited to such gear as they can scavenge or pillage from other races. They have a crude language of sorts, which consists mainly of growls, howling and barking sounds.

The Beastmen range the length and breadth of Golarin in mounted bands of up to forty or so individuals, stopping to rest or make camp in the ruined cities which lie scattered across the plains. They are quite unparticular with regard to their eating habits, having an equal fondness for herd beast, carrion or luckless travelers. Beastmen sometimes hunt men purely for sport, but only in times when food is plentiful.

When on the hunt, a band of Beastmen behaves much like a pack of wild dogs. They will pursue prey relentlessly, driving their darkmanes on and harrying their victims until they become weak with exhaustion. Though fierce when encountered in numbers, they have seldom been known for individual courage. Beastmen are superior trackers, however, and will never quit a blood trail.

The ruined cities of this region provide a strong temptation to explorers, adventurers, and all others who view gainful employment as some sort of accursed malady. Hundreds come each year, alone or in groups, to seek their fortune. Most have little to rely on for direction save a hastily scribbled copy of the Phaedran scholar Erastes' famous treatise, "Secrets of the Past." In this rather long-winded monograph, Erastes claims that the ruined cities hold the following: "The gilded tomb of Irkhan, the mysterious elixirs of immortality, the soulstones of the four blind savants of ancient Acimera, a great crystal golem named Satur, the Nine Books of Knowledge, the treasure-horde of Minra the miser, and the mummified body of the great dragon, Orrix." As Erastes makes no mention of where these purported treasures are to be found (or even what some of them are) many modern-day scholars have branded him a sensationalist; the term "fraud" has also been considered. Still, fortune hunters continue to come to Golarin, though none of Erastes' stated treasures have ever yet been found.

THE QUAN EMPIRE

Beyond the Volcanic Hills and the Jade Mountains lies the great Quan Empire, a land of many and diverse qualities. Its territories are vast, extending from the southern jungles bordering Chana to the northern reaches of the Opal Mountains. Once home to numerous, rival warrior clans, the region came under control of the Quan around the beginning of the New Age. By various, devious means, the Quan eliminated most of their rivals, retaining only such clans as could be coerced or bribed into serving them. In ascending order of importance to the Empire, the clans are: the Vajra, the Sunra, the Mandala, the Kang, and the Quan ruling class.

The Vajra are a race of miners and builders, short and squat in stature, with barrel-like torsos and heavy limbs. Their bodies are covered with overlapping, orange-brown plates similar in appearance to a pangolin. For many centuries, the Vajra occupied the mountains and hills of northern Quan. They constructed great tunnel-complexes, built underground fortress-cities, and mined precious stones and metals.

The Quan invaded their territories in force, taking the normally peaceful Vajra by surprise. The Vajra fought valiantly, but were simply overwhelmed by the superior numbers of their foes. Faced with the extinction of their race, the Vajra relented, becoming the first subjects of Quan. They now serve their conquerors as miners, engineers, stone workers, and low-class infantry. The gold and gemstones received from the Vajra's mines have made the Quan among the wealthiest of Talislanta's peoples.

The Sunra are a semi-aquatic race of humanoids who live in the fabulous Coral City of Isalis, located in the Inland Sea of southern Quan. They are elegant creatures, graceful in stature, with silvery-scaled skin and deep blue eyes. Skilled navigators, the Sunra once ranged the Far Seas from the Crescent Isles to Thaecia. In their glittering dragon barques, they hunted sea dragons, and traded with the people of the Floating City of Oceanus.

The Quan conquered the Sunra by using Vajra engineers to dam the River Shan, sole tributary of the Inland Sea. Rather than allow the Inland Sea to be reduced to a salt marsh, the Sunra accepted the rulership of the Quan. Sunra fishermen and sea farmers now provide the Quan Empire with much of its food. In their ornate dragon barques (two-masted sailing vessels built to resemble sea dragons), the Sunra serve as the naval branch of the Quan military. They are the finest sailors, using intricately designed astrolabes to navigate according to the position of Talislanta's two suns and seven moons.

The Mandalans are a golden-skinned folk, slender of build and hairless, with almond eyes and pleasant features. They created an advanced and enlightened culture, centered amidst the pastel spires, arches and promenades of the stately coastal city of Jacinth. A race of scholars and savants, the Mandalans abhorred violence, considering militarism to be the domain of unsophisticated and primitive peoples. The Quan, sailing in the dragon barques of the Sunra, laid siege to Jacinth from the sea and threatened to burn the city to the ground if the Mandalans did not surrender. Having no navy or army of their own, the Mandalans meekly complied. They serve the Quan as artisans, architects, and historians, among other, lesser duties. Finding the Mandalans to be extremely passive, the Quan also employ them as servants, gardeners, and menial laborers.

The Kang are a tall and fierce people with fiery-red skin, white, pupil-less eyes, and almost reptilian features. They wear their long, black hair pulled straight back in a single queue, iron collars and armbands being the fashion among their warriors. Mounted on the large, bi-pedal lizards known as striders, the nomadic Kang clans dominated the dreary plains of the Grey Lands for many centuries. The Quan, surveying the black iron-clad hosts of the Kang, decided against engaging their red-skinned rivals on the field of battle. Instead, they sent Mandalan emissaries bearing gifts to the Kang war chieftains.

For seven days, the Mandalans delivered wagonload after wagonload of gold, silver, and gemstones, until a small mountain of treasure stood at the feet of the amazed leaders of the Kang. A captain of the Quan army, attired in armor of gold leaf, then rode up on a similarly caparisoned steed. "This is but the smallest portion of the wealth of the Quan Empire," he said. "Join with us against our enemies, and you will become rich men." The Kang war chieftains accepted the offer without hesitation, becoming mercenary subjects of the Quan Empire.

The Quan themselves are a pale-skinned folk of average height and build. Once a barbarian people, they now exhibit the lofty airs and delicate sensibilities normally associated with royalty. They are an unexceptional race, possessing little in the way of intelligence or creativity, but being sufficiently aggressive and cunning to rule an empire. The Quan do not work, but simply oversee the various peoples that their ancestors conquered, who together supply them with all their needs. Even the lowliest Quan dress in costly silk garments, the elite of their kind being notable for the most extravagant and garish costumes: elaborate head dresses festooned with baubles, capes of such length that they must be carried by attendants, and so forth. Jewelry of the most ostentatious sort is considered a mark of distinction and elegance, and obesity a sign of wealth and success. From birth, the Quan are attended hand and foot by slaves, who feed them, bathe them, and carry them about on cushioned palanquins.

Quan society is governed by a rigidly enforced caste system which divides the populace into distinct classes. In descending order, these are: the Grand Elite (the Emperor of Quan and his family), the High Elite (Quan of favored status), the Elite (all other Quan), the Honorary Elite (non-Quan, granted upper class status as a reward for exceptional service; only pure-blood Quan may ever advance beyond this rank), Luminaries (seven separate orders of ascending rank by which non-Quan may advance in status), Kang, Mandalan, Sunra, Vajra, and undesirables (thieves, miscreants, and foreigners).

By careful manipulation of this system, the ruling Quan classes maintain control of the population, rewarding those most loyal to the regime. The Kang, turned into fawning, obsequious puppets by their greed for gold, serve most loyally. They will do almost anything to achieve the exalted rank of Honorary Elite, and are renowned throughout the realm as plotters and schemers of the first order. The Quan employ them in nearly all branches of the military, and to keep the lower classes in line.

There are seven major settlements in Quan: the capitol city of Tian, the coastal city of Jacinthe, Isalis, and the military outposts of Karang, Vishana, Shonan and Hadran. Tian, also known as "The Golden City," is built on an island. Situated amidst a man-made lake fed by waters diverted from the River Shan, the city can only be reached by boat. Tian was designed by Mandalan architects at the command of the Emperor of Quan, who demanded that the capitol of Quan surpass in beauty even the Mandalan city of Jacinth. It is considered by many to be the most splendid city on the continent. The gilded spires and domes of the Palace of a Thousand Fountains, wherein the Emperor resides, is especially notable.

The coastal city of Jacinthe, once the center of Mandalan culture, is now a great resort area used by the wealthiest of the Quan ruling class. A large part of the Mandalan population still lives here, serving as slaves of the Quan Empire. In Jacinth are found gardens of crystal dendrons, mosses and prismatic blossoms, and ancient collections of scrolls and books, few of which are ever used anymore. Elite units of the Kang Dragons guard the city from attack by land, and Sunra warships patrol the harbor, where Quan pleasure barges ply the peaceful waters.

Of Quan's other settlements: The Coral City of Isalis, besides being home to the majority of Quan's Sunra population, serves as the Empire's foremost naval installation. Quan's vast flotilla of dragon barques is stationed around the city, which is accessible only by three outlets of the Shan River. Sunra sea-farmers ply the shallows, harvesting kelp, algae, and other aquatic foodstuffs. Moonfish, rare creatures reserved by law for the ruling class Quan, are caught here and shipped to Tian in water-filled spheres of colored glass. A contingent of Kang troops maintains order and discipline.

Karang, located to the north, is a walled citadel built by the Vajra to safeguard against incursions of barbaric Harakin from across the Opal Mountains. Much of Quan's Vajra population lives in this ponderous structure, which is criss-crossed with catecombs and tunnels after the Vajra style. Precious stones and metals from the Vajra's mines are stored here until they can be shipped by caravan to Shonan and Tian. Kang trackers patrol the border regions with tarkus, their deadly hunting beasts.

Vishana, located in the hot and humid jungles of the far south, is a military outpost of some importance to the Empire. A barrier of wooden stakes surrounds the fortress, which is situated near the mouth of the River Shan. It can also be reached by road, though the way is made difficult by the presence of wild beasts and Witchmen from the Jungles of Chana. Several garrisons of Kang trackers and cavalry operate from Vishana, patroling and keeping safe the Empire's southern borders. All wish they were somewhere else. A number of Mandalans serve here, gathering rare herbs for shipment to the north. Articles taken in battle with the Chana Witchmen are also in demand, including trained wrist-vipers, magical adjuncts and shrunken heads.

Shonan is primarily a military installation, though it also serves as a center of trade and as home to many of the Kang. It is located at a nexus of the River Shan and the Emperor's Road, with a bridge nearby. Built of dull grey stone from the Volcanic Hills, Shonan is surrounded by a forty-foot wall lined with rows of black iron spikes. It is an impregnable fortress which has withstood countless attacks by the Sauran tribes, who dwell to the west. Hundreds of troops are stationed here, including Kang trackers, cavalry, Elite units and Vajra artillerists and engineers. Goods of many sorts pass through Shonan: precious metals, gemstones and cerulean dye from Karang, foodstuffs and moonfish transported up the River Shan from Isalis, rare herbs and hardwoods from Vishana, and fine Mandalan silkcloth from Jacinthe. Kang warriors often take their leave in Shonan, hoping to impress the fiery Kang women with tales of their heroic exploits.

The Citadel of Hadran is the largest military installation in the Empire, housing thousands of Kang troops, striders and support personnel. Built of marbled green and black stone from the Jade Mountains, Hadran serves as the headquarters of the Overlord, the supreme commander of the Kang, subject only to the Emperor himself. The forces stationed here are responsible for the security of the Bridge at Hadran, a massive structure which spans a great chasm some six hundred feet in depth. Hadran is the gateway to the Quan Empire, strategically important from any of several different points of view; the bridge allows access to the west as well, a source of some concern to Rajanistan, Carantheum and Faradun.

Despite an outward appearance of civility, the Quan rule their empire with merciless precision. Most criminal offenses are punishable by death, a variety of cruel methods being employed to achieve the desired result. Individuals accused of breaking the law are typically hauled before a Kang magistrate and sentenced without trial. As it is impossible for individuals to bring charges of any sort against a person of higher rank or social status, injustice is rife among the less privileged classes. Those seeking to elude the Quan's brand of justice are hunted down by Kang trackers and their beasts, who are said to be most efficient.

The Quan have no political or religious affiliations, the two concepts being without interest to these folk, who consider themselves akin to gods. Although they tend to be distrustful of strangers, the Quan are not entirely averse to doing business with foreigners. Imrian coracles sometimes sail to Jacinth to buy or sell slaves, and merchants from Djaffa, Farad and the Seven Kingdoms compete for trade contracts in the cities of Hadran and Shonan. No foreigner may travel across the Empire without first obtaining an official permit, however. Issued in the form of a lead tablet stamped with the Emperor's seal, these devices are available at Hadran and Jacinth, and cost upwards of one thousand gold lumens apiece.

My experience with the Quan was, by all accounts, uncharacteristically pleasant, and for a time quite profitable. I was traveling along the Emperor's Road, some hundred and thirty miles from the capitol of Tian, when a heavily armed troop of Kang warriors ordered my wagon off the highway. My questions regarding the reason for this delay were met with a meaningful show of weapons. In the interest of self-preservation, I acceded to the local protocol and kept further utterances to myself.

The reason for these procedures soon became apparent. From far off in the distance came the trumpeting of horns, accompanied by the strident sounds of cymbals and gongs. A great procession came slowly into view, trundling its way towards Tian: dancers in Mandalan silks, musicians in colorful raiment, cushioned litters perched atop the backs of giant ogriphants, carriages decorated in gold leaf and jade, and a thousand of the Kang's elite dragon cavalry dressed in full battle armor. At the center of this festive entourage rode the Emperor himself, his mode of conveyance a spectacular, gilded tower drawn by four crested dragons.

As the procession passed slowly by, I thought to see the Emperor cast an idle glance in my direction, then turn to mutter something to his advisors, who hovered about him in the manner of sycophants. A few minutes later, twelve Kang warriors surrounded my wagon and ordered me to follow at the rear of the Emperor's entourage. Keeping in mind my earlier encounter with the Kang, I nodded and complied.

We arrived in the capitol four days later, whereupon I was brought before the Emperor of Quan. Slaves carried in the contents of my wagon, mainly curios from the Western Lands and a few artifacts gleaned from the ruined cities of the Wilderlands. The Emperor's advisors examined these articles, discarding some and taking others to the Emperor for his inspection. Not a word was spoken to me during this time, causing me no little apprehension with regard to the ultimate fate of myself and my wares. The Emperor, without bothering even to acknowledge my presence, motioned casually to his elite Kang guards, signifying that the audience had come to a close.

I was then escorted out of the hall, down a long corridor, and into an elegantly furnished anteroom. Here, much to my relief, I was informed by a translator that the Emperor had been favorably impressed with my collection of curios. Marking me as an accomplished explorer, the great tyrant had decided that I would be sent to the far corners of the Empire, there to gather information about these faraway lands. A troop of Kang warriors and a female Mandalan guide would accompany me, all reasonable expenses to be paid by the Quan Empire. As there was no indication that I was to be given a choice in the matter, I accepted the Emperor's offer. Thus did I meet the beautiful Zen, and embark upon a series of further travels lasting some two and a half years.

In addition to the Empire's sizeable humanoid population, many strange creatures dwell in the land of Quan. Shriekers, terrible metal-plumed birds, haunt the Cerulean Forests of the northern sector, as do yaksha and muskront. Wild striders, tarkus and winged azoryl prowl the Greylands, where crested dragons are sometimes found. The southern jungles are to be avoided, for reasons mentioned earlier and due to the infrequent appearance of multi-headed kaliya. The River Shan and the waters of the Inland Sea and coastal regions are somewhat more benign. Nevertheless, the smart traveler will keep an eye out for lurkers, rainbow kra, and grey ikshada, which are not unknown in these parts.

RAJANISTAN

P.D. BREEDING © 86

Far to the east, beyond the scorching sands of the Red Desert, lies the warlike nation of Rajanistan. It is a harsh and arid land, made hospitable only by numerous small oases found scattered across its far-ranging territories. The Jade Mountains form its southern border, merging in a northward-sweeping arc with the treacherous Volcanic Hills. Elsewhere, the terrain is monotonous in form, a sprawling expanse of yellow sand interrupted only by patches of date-palm, nettle, and briarbush.

Known as "the Scourge of the Desert Kingdoms," Rajanistan is the most populous of the eastern lands. Many nomadic tribes make their home here, including the Aramut, Zagir, Shadinn, and the Virds. The rulers of this country, however, are the Rajans: fierce, dark-skinned folk, tall and wiry of build, with diabolical features, horn-like protrusions jutting forth from the chin and forehead, and blood-red eyes. They dress in dark grey capes, veiled head dresses, and loose-fitting garments bound with cords at the wrists, ankles, and waist. These cords, made of braided linen, are used for many practical purposes by the Rajans, including the strangling of enemies. It is the unfriendly custom of both the males and females to carry concealed weapons on their persons, curved daggers being considered especially elegant. The Aramut and Zagir are shorter in stature, and favor less elaborate attire, while the Shadinn are veritable giants, averaging nearly seven feet in height. The Virds, a mongrel people, are devoid of any single set of definable characteristics.

The Rajans are a race of fanatics, utterly devoted to the Khadun, absolute ruler of Rajanistan and Necromancer-Priest of the Black Mystic Cult (the official religion of the state). His followers claim that the Khadun is the earthly manifestation of the dread entity known as Death, and revere him as a demi-god. They believe that only by dying can they be one in spirit with their mystic ruler, and so are eager to sacrifice their lives for any cause that he endorses. Along the same line of reasoning, the Rajans claim that by killing non-believers, they convert them to their morbid and insane religion. Members of the cult are called the Followers of Urmaan (see **History**).

A warlike and violent people, the Rajans long ago conquered and subjugated the other nomadic tribes of the region. Employing the vanquished peoples as slave labor, the Rajans built Irdan, a massive fortress constructed of stones hauled from the Jade Mountains. Irdan is the only permanent settlement in Rajanistan, and serves as the country's capitol. Untold thousands of troops —"numerous as the desert sands," or so it is said—are stationed in and around the fortress: mail-clad Rajan elite cavalry, Aramut lancers, Zagir archers, Shadinn armored land lizard units, and scimitar-wielding Vird infantry.

The Rajans have long coveted the lands which lie to the west, particularly the ore-rich sands of the Red Desert. Despite several attempts to wrest control of this region from Carantheum, the Rajans have never been able to accomplish this goal. Defeat has never swayed them from this cause, however; the Khadun has sworn to crush Carantheum if every man, woman and child in Rajanistan must die in the attempt. As the Rajan generals are unfortunately renowned more for their fanatical obedience to the Khadun than their tactical abilities, outside observers have speculated that such a result is well within the realm of possibilities.

More effective are the Necromancers of the Black Mystic Cult, who dwell within the Temple of Death in Irdan. They wear dark ritual vestments and skull-like, iron masks. Those of great power claim to be capable of manifesting a third eye in the center of the forehead, purportedly of use in detecting invisible or spirit presences. The Necromancers protect the Khadun, and are responsible for training the elite corps of torturers and assassins known as the Torquar. Under the personal command of the Khadun, the Torquar export terrorism and subterfuge to many lands. Its members are known for their skill with various unusual weapons, including the Da-Khar (leather gauntlets equipped with retractable metal claws).

Rajanistan has few marketable resources, but is rich in gold, which is mined by slave labor and transported by caravan from the Jade Mountains to the fortress city of Irdan. The Rajans use their gold to purchase weapons, slaves, and narcotic herbs from Faradun, the only nation with whom the Rajans have any sort of trade ties. No other business is done in Irdan, as the Rajans do not fancy foreign merchants in their country.

The nomadic Djaffir merchant tribes do not take kindly to this attitude, which they consider a restraint of trade. Consequently, they and their bandit brethren will seldom pass up an opportunity to "pull the beards of the Rajans" (as they like to put it). Having spent some time with one of the smaller merchant tribes, I can personally attest to the vehemence with which the Djaffir pursue such activities.

I am reminded of an incident which occurred at the eastern edge of the Wilderlands of Zaran. The tribe I had been riding with was known to do business with the Kang, mercenary protectors of the Quan Empire. To do so, the Djaffir had to follow a circuitous route through the Volcanic Hills to the Kang installation at Hadran. The only alternative to this was to trespass through a heavily patrolled sector of Rajanistan, risking encounters with the Rajans enroute to the bridge at Hadran. Naturally, the Djaffir always chose the latter approach, rationalizing that this was the shortest and least time-consuming route to Hadran.

On this particular occasion, the tribe decided that they would show their utter disdain for the Rajans by venturing into their territories during broad daylight. I assured them that they need not be so bold merely to impress me, which they considered a grand joke. On the next day, we rose before dawn and approached within a mile of the Rajanistan border. There we waited, mounted on our swift ontra, a cool night wind blowing at our backs. When Talislanta's twin suns finally broke across the horizon, the tribe's chieftain raised his scimitar and let forth an exultant cry. The rest of the tribe replied in kind, and we were off, thundering across the plains and into Rajanistan.

The first Rajans we encountered were a band of Aramut, barely risen from their sleep. Led by our chieftain, we rode straight through the Aramut encampment, the Djaffir capsizing tents and slashing indiscriminately with their blades as they went. We were gone before the Aramut knew what had transpired, leaving their camp in complete disorder.

Riding at breakneck speed, we next came upon a company of Virds, with much the same result. The Djaffir were wild with the thrill of battle, and becoming ever more bold with each passing mile. At the sight of a Rajan merchant caravan, the nomads shouted in unison some deprecating remark. They descended upon their rivals, wreaking havoc upon the Rajans' baggage trains before again dashing off towards Hadran.

This last incident aroused the attention of a patroling contingent of Rajan cavalry, who set off after us in hot pursuit. When the bridge at Hadran finally came into view, my heart leapt with joy, then just as quickly sank; blocking the bridge was a unit of Shadinn land lizards, armed to the teeth. With the Rajans at our heels and the Shadinn ahead, our doom seemed imminent.

The Djaffir, though certainly aware of our plight, continued to ride at full gallop towards the bridge. The Shadinn responded, charging forth on their armored lizards to meet us head on. This, evidently, was what the Djaffir had hoped would occur. Scattering like leaves on the wind, the nomads rode in between and around the Shadinn's lumbering beasts, who nearly fell over themselves trying to match the agile maneuvers of the Djaffir's swift steeds. Some of the Djaffir threw their cloaks over the heads of the land lizards, creating further confusion; others let loose with their short bows, leaving riderless lizards in their wake.

The pursuing Rajan cavalry arrived on the scene only to become hopelessly entangled with the Shadinn host, which by this time was in a state of utter disarray. In the ensuing crush of Rajans, land lizards, and Shadinn, the nomads were able to make the bridge. Four of our group had suffered slight wounds, a small price to pay for such sport, at least in the opinion of the Djaffir.

Under the iron rule of the Khadun, Rajanistan is among the most repressive states in Talislanta. The punishment for most crimes is the removal of an appropriate body part: liars have their tongues cut off, thieves lose a hand, voyeurs (those who attempt to peek beneath a Rajan woman's veil) lose an eye. The penalty for adultery is said to be especially grim. Individuals accused of treason or heresy (the two offenses are virtually interchangeable, given the make-up of the Rajan government) are imprisoned in the dreaded Tower of Irdan, where the Rajan torturers and Inquisitors practice their arts.

Rajanistan has political ties with no other nation, except perhaps Faradun. The presence of the Rajan hordes remains an impediment to east-west land trade, a situation favorable to Faradun, and one which some suggest the Farad would like to perpetuate. Rajan marks Carantheum and Djaffa as hated foes, and bears no love for the Seven Kingdoms. Only the Volcanic Hills and the hostile Sauran tribes separate Rajanistan from the Quan Empire, a condition which some view as a boon, given the Quan's history of expansion and conquest.

The mountains and deserts of Rajanistan are rife with dangerous beasts, including yaksha and sand demons, respectively. Crested dragons, though somewhat rare, are not unknown in these parts, immature specimens being much favored by the Rajan Necromancers for use as steeds. During the spring months, water from thawing ice caps cascades down the Jade Mountains, carrying with it many small bits and chunks of gold. Adventurers with a flair for the melodramatic sometimes attempt to steal into the mountains disguised as Rajans, thereby hoping to become rich. Those who survive this perilous endeavor, in fact, occasionally do.

The territories designated as the Seven Kingdoms represent a loosely organized confederation of seven separate city states, each ruled by its own king. Established during the New Age by the descendants of various peoples displaced by the Great Disaster, the Seven Kingdoms share a common government, known as the Council of Kings. Each has its own national color, and retains all the customs and traditions peculiar to its inhabitants. The seven member nations of this unique confederation are: Cymril, Durne, Sindar, Astar, Taz, Vardune and Kasmir.

Cymril is the erstwhile capitol of the Seven Kingdoms, this due as much to the country's central location as anything else. Here dwell the Cymrilians, the descendants of a race of wizards and magicians exiled long ago from the now-defunct Phaedran dynasty. Tall and slender in stature, they have pale green skin and hair, with golden eyes and placid features. There are no prerequisites regarding fashion; all types of exotic apparel are in vogue, though magicians continue to favor the high-collared cloaks worn by their ancient ancestors, the Phandre.

Sweeping hills and light forest dominate much of the Cymrilian countryside, which is largely uninhabited. The greatest part of the population lives in the enchanting capitol of Cymril, a city of convoluted spires and archways constructed almost entirely of green glass. Here, the Cymrilian magicians practice their arts, creating wondrous windships (sail-powered vessels which ride the winds), potions, powders and other magical adjuncts. Cymril's artisans are unsurpassed in the Western Lands, and are the continent's leading suppliers of amberglass, a crystalline substance with numerous practical uses in the field of magic. Caravans from many lands come here to trade for Cymrilian wares, aquavit (an expensive Cymrilian liqueur), and goods from across the Seven Kingdoms.

The ruler of Cymril is known as the Wizard King. Usually the most capable of Cymril's spell casters, the Wizard King is elected by popular vote, and serves a term of two or three years. If he is a reasonable sort of fellow, the populace will allow the Wizard King to remain in power for the full term. Once each year, the city of Cymril hosts the Magical Fair, a colorful spectacle lasting two weeks and attended by folk from all across Talislanta. The national color of Cymril is green, a not surprising choice considering the monochromatic Cymrilian pigmentation.

Astar is a land of sylvan glades, lakes and streams. Here dwell the last of an ancient and enchanting race of beings known as the Muses. Nymph-like creatures believed to be of magical origin, the Muses are the most beautiful of the humanoid races. Their bodies are slender and lithe, their features delicate and exquisitely fashioned. They dress in translucent gowns, shaded in hues complementing the colors of their butterfly-like wings, skin and hair: pastel blue, aquamarine, turquoise, violet, and rose, to name just a few.

The Muses of Astar are by nature flighty and irresponsible. Most are content to lay about, dreaming secret dreams, sipping the nectar of flowers, or gazing at butterflies, birds, and Muses of the opposite sex. As the mood suits them, they may project a thought, an idea, or a mental picture to another Muse or some other creature. All Muses possess this unusual ability, the range and scope of which supposedly increase with practice. The Muses have no settlements, but tend to congregate in small groups scattered throughout the scenic woodlands of Astar. They possess a natural talent for all artistic pursuits, and create enchanting musical instruments, tapestries of colored gossamer and other fine goods, but only when stricken by inspiration.

The Muses of Astar have no king or queen, but draw straws once each month to determine who is to represent their people at the Council of Kings in Cymril. The holder of the short straw is crowned king or queen, as the situation dictates. Though some few of curious bent become adventurers, most Muses are quite content to spend their lives in Astar. Were it not for the occasional visitor from Thaecia (whose people greatly admire the Muses' telepathic talents) or other parts of the Seven Kingdoms, few Muses would know anything of the rest of Talislanta. The national color of Astar is azure, probably for no good reason, but possibly in honor of nearby Lake Zephyr, a favorite trysting spot of the Muses.

Vardune is a densely forested region bordering the Axis River to the west. Its inhabitants, the Ardua, are a race in the process of devolving from an avian to a ground-dwelling species. The Ardua's vestigal wings, once used for flying, have atrophied from disuse. For the majority of Ardua, these appendages are more decorative than functional, though some still use them for gliding.

There are two sub-species of Ardua: Green Ardua, who seldom exceed five feet in height, and the taller and somewhat more aggressive Blue Ardua. Both species are slender and frail in stature, and have skin which glistens with a metallic sheen. A crested cox-comb of feathers adds to the distinctive appearance of these folk. By contrast, their manner of dress is simple and austere, and includes a short tunic and cape of plain viridian linen.

Formerly a race of sky-roving hunters and gatherers, the Ardua were forced to abandon their traditional way of life when their ancestral homeland was annexed by the forces of the old Phaedran regime. They settled in the forests of Vardune and built a number of small settlements along the eastern banks of the Axis River. The Blue Ardua, hunters by trade, became the protectors of their race; the Green Ardua, with their knowledge of seeds and fruiting plants, became horticulturists. They soon adapted to their new existence, and their settlements grew and prospered.

The largest of the Ardua's settlements is the River City of Vashay, renowned as a producer of useful herbs and plants. Vashay's most important crop is viridia, a giant species of pod-bearing plant. The breathtaking bridge at Vashay and the triple-tiered terrace dwellings of the Ardua are all made of woven viridia tendrils, as are many other products sold in this region. The plant's ten-foot long pods are filled with a fibrous down which can be spun into cloth (called viridian linen); the pods themselves, when cured, cut to specifications and lacquered, are of use in the making of small skiffs, wagons and roofing materials. The ruler of the Ardua is the River King, who may be either a Blue or Green Ardua. The national color of Vardune is aqua-blue.

VASHAY

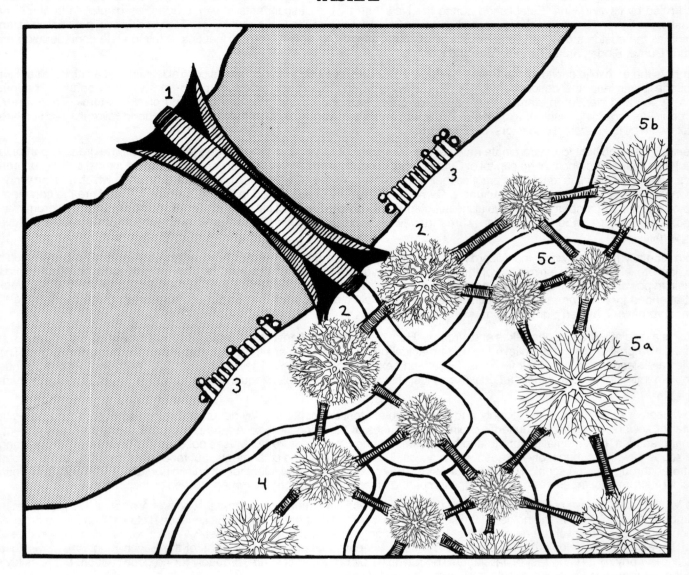

The river settlement of Vashay is a typical example of Ardua construction. Giant viridia trees form the foundation of the settlement. Mats of woven viridia tendrils are used to create the three-tiered Ardua tree-dwellings, which are connected one to the other by elevated walkways of intricately woven vines. The lower levels of these dwellings are accessible from the ground by means of sturdy wooden ramps; the upper tiers, by spiral stairways built around the trunk of the viridia tree. Trellises of flowering vines serve as the outer walls of the dwelling, forming living "walls" of varying color and scent.

1) Bridge at Vashay: This structure is made of viridia-wood and woven viridia tendrils. It is wide enough to accommodate two wagons traveling abreast of each other, and is superbly maintained by Green Ardua horticulturists (living viridia trees form the bridge's footings).

2) Toll Stations: These twin tree-dwellings serve as watchtowers and toll stations. Platoons of twenty Blue Ardua, armed with crescent knives and dart-throwers, are stationed at each. A toll of one gold lumen per beast or conveyance is charged here. Individuals traveling on foot may pass without charge.

3) Docks: Blue Ardua river patrols moor their barge-forts at these facilities. The northern docks are used by private craft, including merchant vessels and tour-barges.

4) Barracks: Blue Ardua river and forest patrols are housed here.

5) Trader's Haven: This is a sizeable establishment consisting of five tree-dwellings. These are:

a) River Supply: Goods bought and sold here include foodstuffs, timber, viridia pod-craft, metal tools and implements, travelers' raiment and gear, etc.

b) The River Tavern: An inn and tavern catering primarily to Ardua. Prices are average, and quality—by Ardua standards—is supposedly good.

c) River Inns: Three establishments offering rooms for rent.

Durne is a land of grassy knolls, gently rising hills, and sparse woodlands. The folk who live here, known as the Gnomekin, are a diminutive race of humanoids who average just over three feet in height. They have nut-brown complexions, muscular bodies, and wide-eyed, almost child-like features. Both the males and females have a crest of soft, black fur running from the center of the forehead to the small of the back. Despite their small size, the Gnomekin of Durne are quite strong, and are as agile and sure-footed as mountain goats. Their language sounds much like the purring of cats.

The Gnomekin have but a single settlement, the subterranean city of Durne. Constructed some two hundred feet below ground, the settlement consists of numerous cave dwellings connected by a complex maze of tunnels. Large caverns are used for the growing of mushrooms and tubers, underground lakes serving as hatcheries for several species of subterranean fish and molluscs. The Gnomekin also grow amber crystals, raw materials useful in the making of magical orbs and scrying devices. Durne is ruled by an hereditary monarch known as the Gnome-King, a personage of some local renown. He is responsible for determining fair prices for the goods produced by his peoples, which are delivered by underground trail to Cymril once each month. Additionally, the Gnome-King is commander-in-chief of the country's small but feisty army. The national color of Durne is brown, coincidentally the favorite color of the Gnomekin.

Kasmir is an arid region bordered to the south by the Jaspar Mountains and to the east by the Wilderlands of Zaran. The folk who live here, called the Kasmir, are short and lean, with odd-looking shriveled features. They dress in hooded cloaks, loose robes and sandals, and carry concealed weapons (such as spring-knives and blade staves) on their persons at all times.

The Kasmir are a wealthy people, though how they acquired their fortune is unknown; some say they were once partners of the Djaffir. Whatever their history, the Kasmir are renowned throughout the continent as misers. Their metalsmiths construct the most ingenious and elaborate locking mechanisms, traps and vaults. Kasmir money lenders and appraisers are unexcelled in their craft. They finance caravans, purchase and re-sell large quantities of goods, and lend money to fund ventures of many different sorts, typically at somewhat high rates. The Djaffir merchant tribes, who still do business with the Kasmir from time to time, commonly refer to them as "Tu-Beshal" (meaning "blood-suckers," though the term carries certain lewd connotations as well).

The capitol city of Kasmir is a veritable fortress, guarded by mercenary Thralls from Taz. Here the Kasmir live in windowless stone towers, their doors barred and locked against thieves. The ruler of these people, known simply as the King of Kasmir, holds his job only as long as the wealthy Kasmir money-changers feel he is effectively representing their best interests. Should he fail to live up to their expectations, the King is beheaded and a new ruler chosen. Despite the high pay and numerous perquisites, the position of King is one which few Kasmir aspire to. The national color of Kasmir is purple, an elegant hue popular among all the people of this land.

Taz is a land of thick jungle fading into the swampy mire of neighboring Mog. Here live the strange race of humanoids known as the Thralls. Bred by the sorcerers of some ancient and forgotten kingdom as an army of slave warriors, the Thralls are tall and muscular of build. Hairless and devoid of pigmentation, they are distinguishable only by sex; otherwise, all Thralls look exactly alike. In defiance of this inbred genetic trait, the Thralls decorate their bodies from head to toe with wildly elaborate tattoos, thereby attaining some degree of individuality.

The Thralls of Taz live in great communal complexes constructed of cut stone blocks, all of which look very much alike. Bred for combat, the Thralls know no other life. Most serve as protectors of the Seven Kingdoms, guarding the various border regions or working as sentinels, caravan guards, and so on. Those of a more creative nature sometimes hire out as mercenaries. The Thralls are ruled by an individual known as the Warrior-King (or Queen, as the case may be) of Taz. The position is open to challenge by duel once every year, the winner being accorded ruling status. The national color of Taz is crimson, or blood red.

Sindar is a land of towering mesas, arches, and strange configurations of time-worn stone. Underground springs and geysers are the only sources of water in this region, which is bordered to the east by the barren canyons of the Dead River. The folk who live here are known as the Sindarans. They stand over seven feet in height, are emaciated in build, and have wrinkled, sandy-colored skin. Sindarans have a row of horn-like nodules running from the crown of the head to the back of the neck, dividing the brain into two independently operating organs. Their earlobes are long and distended, and a curved spur of bone protrudes from beneath the chin.

The Sindarans live in small communes, each situated atop a large mesa or some similarly prominent topographical feature. Their dwellings are elegant tiered structures built of carved stone blocks and hardwoods imported from Vardune and Taz. Gossamer curtains, dyed various shades of orange and burnt umber, serve as the outer walls of the Sindarans' structures. Billowing gracefully in the warm breezes, the curtains provide a measure of privacy while retaining a feeling of wide-open spaces. Communication between Sindaran communes is possible by means of large, reflective crystals, mounted on tripodal stands and used to flash messages from one outpost to the next. In this way, information may be passed rapidly throughout the country.

The Sindarans are renowned as collectors, from menageries of rare beasts to ancient scrolls, coins, curios and objects of art. To finance their private collections, they create fine wares of silver and precious stones (both common in the region), which they sell for gold in Cymril. When not preoccupied with their collections, Sindarans enjoy playing Trivarian, a complex game which other races find incomprehensible. The drinking of Skoryx, a potent liquor of rare qualities, is also a favored pastime. The national color of Sindar is orange.

At the eastern border of Kasmir is a great stone bridge which spans the yawning chasm known as the Dead River. Built by the Sindarans, the bridge is exceptionally sturdy, but a bit narrow. It will accommodate only a single wagon, or perhaps three mounted men riding abreast of one another, at a time. As such, large caravans can sometimes cause considerable delays when attempting to traverse the span. A toll of one gold lumen per person five gold lumens per wagon or other conveyance) is collected by mercenary Thrall guards, stationed night and day at a fortified complex adjacent to the bridge. Alternatives to this costly route are limited to the free bridges at Sindar and Danuvia, both of which are constructed along similar lines.

The Seven Kingdoms' Council of Kings meets once a month at the Royal Palace in Cymril. Though relations between the member nations are usually good, the seven kings seem to be constantly squabbling over petty laws, tariffs, boundary lines, prices for trade goods, and so forth. A majority vote decides all issues, except in the case of a four-to-three decision, known as an "impasse." Whenever a Council ends in an impasse, there is no official ruling on the subject, and each kingdom is free to establish its own laws and guidelines on the issue in question until the following Council. As might be expected, this often leads to incredible confusion. Laws may change abruptly, curfews or new tariffs may be instituted, and prices for goods or tolls may fluctuate wildly.

Before I met up with the magician Crystabal, I had traveled extensively throughout the Seven Kingdoms. The various countries are each, in their own way, quite scenic. Travel along the Seven Roads can present difficulties, however: be on the alert for winged apes while in Taz, and watch for mandragores, stranglevine and other noxious plant species while visiting Vardune or Astar. Beastmen from nearby Golarin sometimes attempt to cross the Lost River at Sindar, and Za bandit clans may be a source of some concern in Kasmir. In Durne, it is safer below ground than above. Bat-winged stryx and darklings sometimes cross the Obsidian Mountains of Urag and haunt the hills and forests of this region.

Even Cymril itself is not proof from danger. Despite the efforts of Thrall patrols, the woodlands which lie beyond the city proper continue to serve as home to miscreant wizards, highwaymen, and such predators as werebeasts and exomorphs. The civilized versions of these latter menaces, namely peddlers and charlatans, are to be found almost everywhere in Cymril.

Keeping the confederation secure from without, bands of Thralls, mounted on rugged Mangonel Lizards, patrol the northern and eastern borderlands in force. Contingents of Blue Ardua guard the western and southern borders, plying the river in barge-forts and armed with crescent knives and dart throwers. It is little wonder, then, that the Seven Kingdoms are considered among the safest places on the continent.

Altogether, the Seven Kingdoms do not wield great political or military power. The country is important primarily due to its strategic location between the eastern and western lands. As such, a considerable amount of trade passes through the Seven Kingdoms, to the benefit of all concerned.

SINDARAN MESA-SETTLEMENT

The Sindaran mode of construction reflects a thoughtful balance between the appreciation of open spaces and the essential concerns of security and defense. Built high atop the wind-worn mesas of their ancestral homeland, their tiered pavilions can be opened to take advantage of cooling breezes, or closed against the chill night air. The upper levels afford an unimpeded view of the surrounding region. Other features include:

1) Ramp and Loading Platform: This is an accessway for wagons, burden beasts and other conveyances.

2) Lift Platform: This twenty-foot square wooden platform, operated by means of a clever system of winches and counterweights, allows access to the settlement. The platform can be retracted at need; a necessary precaution, given the close proximity of hostile Ur warclans and marauding bands of Beastmen.

3) Crystal: These reflective devices, mounted on movable tri-pods, are used to send messages to other Sindaran settlements.

4) Docking Area: This is a landing area for visiting windships. Generally speaking, only the largest settlements are equipped with such facilities.

5) Hidden Defenses (not shown in diagram): The Sindarans, a folk enamored of subtlety and intrigue, prefer to disguise the defensive capabilities of their settlements. Some of the methods employed to this end include: secret tunnels, through which Sindaran defenders can launch surprise attacks upon forces attempting to lay siege to the mesa-settlement; light ballista, concealed within the upper levels of tiered pavilions, for use vs airborne attackers (such as Stryx); hidden stockpiles of glassine spheres, filled with noxious alchemical compounds, which may be hurled down upon would-be invaders; and trained attack-beasts imported from other lands.

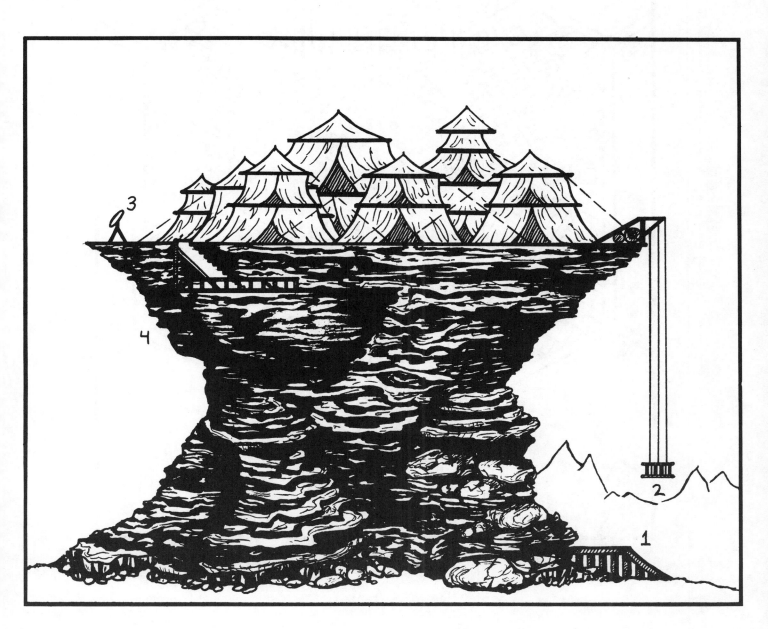

THE CITY OF CYMRIL

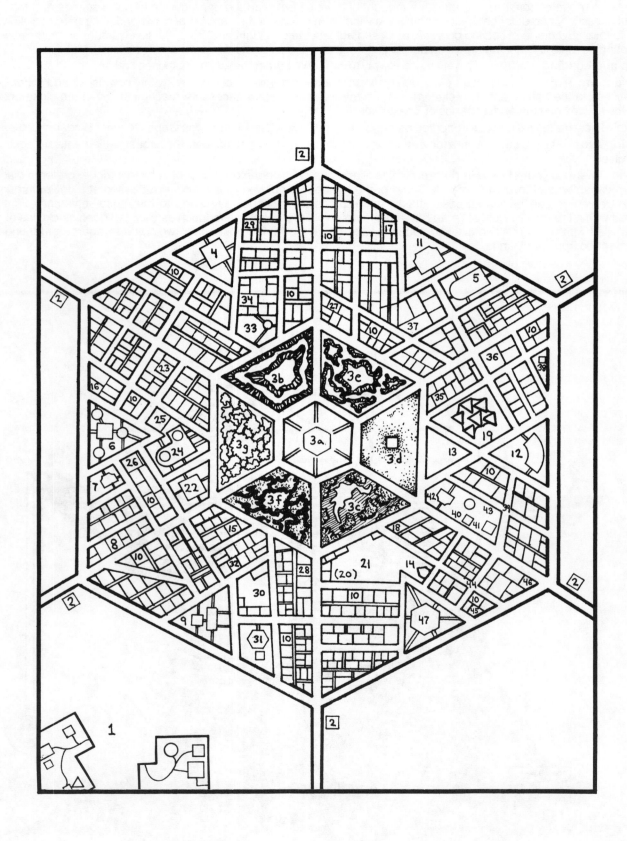

THE CITY OF CYMRIL

The following is a brief outline of the city of Cymril, capitol of the Seven Kingdoms, as described by the wizard Tamerlin. Intended as a guide for travelers from other lands, the outline and accompanying map are by no means to be considered complete. Rather, it would appear that Tamerlin mentioned only such features as he deemed important, or perhaps interesting. The inclusion of certain less-than-reputable establishments in this guide may be construed as an indicator of Tamerlin's habits and preferences, or of those which the wizard ascribed to his readers.

Cymril is a fabulous city of convoluted spires, geodesic domes and arched promenades. Surmounted on all sides by a line of low, grassy hills, the city is located at the nexus of six roads, each leading to one of the other Seven Kingdoms. Beyond the line of hills lie sweeping farmlands and vineyards, with scattered copies of whithergall and deadwood fading at last into the Cymrilian woodlands.

The city itself is a pleasant enough place, provided one is fond of the color green. With few exceptions, most of the city's structures are built of blocks, slabs and beams of translucent green crystal (structures not made of this substance are often simply painted with green lacquers). Cymril imports all its building materials from Faradun, where a sizeable mining installation situated on the shores of the Sea of Glass operates year 'round. The glass miners' guild profits greatly from this eccentric tradition, as does the glass workers' guild, whose artisans create magnificent spirals, fluted columns and other ornamental devices used in construction. The local citizenry, not wishing to clash with their complexions or surroundings, customarily attire themselves in raiment of complementary colors: lemon yellow, sea green, lime, canary yellow, aquamarine, saffron, vermillion, and so on.

The Cymrilian people are descended from the Phandre, a race of magicians and wizards who helped found the old Phaedran Empire. When the First Dynasty was toppled, the Phandre were forced into exile. After a period of wandering, they established a settlement in the woodlands, the somewhat diverse Phandre population coalescing to form the new nation of Cymril. Certain dissident factions objected to the new order, with varying consequences: the Tanasians, formerly of the ruling class, remained haughty and aloof. Some, considered miscreants, went to dwell in solitude in the woodlands. Others consented to live with the majority of the population, but refused Cymrilian citizenship. The Pharesians, a small but vocal minority, objected vehemently to the decision to adopt green as the national color of Cymril. They began wearing bright patchwork coats and multi-hued garments as a sign of protest. When this failed to have any significant impact on public opinion, many took to the roads and became peddlers or mountebanks, where they continue to be a nuisance to travelers.

Apart from these minor difficulties, the Cymrilians are a united and largely prosperous people. A good deal of trade passes through the city, which is a popular stopover point for merchants and caravans headed to and from the western lands. Traders and visitors from the other member nations are especially prevalent, and there is a great tolerance here for different cultural, political, and religious viewpoints.

The laws of the city are similarly enlightened, most being founded upon fairness and logic. As an example, it is illegal to throw stones in the city proper, a reasonable enough stricture given the nature of Cymrilian construction. The punishment for most types of non-violent crime is a period of enforced labor in the glass mines; more serious affronts normally carry a sentence of banishment, typically to some unpleasant extra-dimensional locale.

1) City Outskirts: Surrounding the city are many small farms, vineyards, and country estates, not a few of which exhibit a certain rustic charm. Most of these are owned by Green Ardua, who work the land with exceptional skill. The fruits of their labors are transported by wagon to Cymril, though a small percentage of the crop is sold at roadside stands. Beware of peddlers and mountebanks, who prowl the roads leading into Cymril and the outlying regions.

2) Sentinel Stations: Each of these one-story structures houses a contingent of twenty Thrall mercenaries, armed with greatswords, heavy crossbows, and garde. At least four mangonel lizards are stabled at each of these stations, a provision intended to discourage wandering bandit clans and predatory beasts from the woodlands and beyond. Blue Ardua patrols from the inner city check in at these stations on a regular basis, keeping the Thrall sentinels appraised of security concerns. It is a mistake to underestimate the capabilities of these forces: the Thralls occupying these posts are all experienced veterans from the eastern borderlands, and the Ardua—though slight of build—are uncannily accurate with both the dart-thrower and crescent knife.

3) The Seven Parks: Ringing the city are seven different parks, each artfully designed to depict topographical features representative of one of the Seven Kingdoms. Statues of historical (or otherwise prominent) figures stand at the center of each of the commons. The seven parks are an attraction to tourists, and consequently, to peddlers, musicians, and pick-pockets.

3a) Cymril Park: An attractive garden landscaped with crystalline shrubs, trees, and flowers fashioned of colored glass. Walking paths paved with green glass tiles lead to a central commons. Here stands a crystal statue of Pharos, first wizard king of Cymril, whose extensive writings on magic are preserved at the Lyceum Arcanum (see #24).

3b) Durne Park: An enclosed area built to resemble an underground cavern, complete with scenic grottos and gardens where amber crystals are grown. An amber statue of Sabo Orabio, the Gnomeking who led his people to victory over the Darkling hordes of Urag, stands here. Phosphorescent fungi illuminate the cavern-park, lending a definite Durnean ambience to the surroundings.

3c) Astar Park: A sylvan preserve, replete with fields of rainbow-hued wildflowers, copses of willowood, and a scaled-down version of Lake Zephyr. In the middle of the lake is an island, upon which stands a statue fashioned of lavender blue stone and hung with garlands of blossoms. The statue depicts a Muse; possibly Twysk, a maker of gossamer harps renowned in ancient times, though the Muses claim not to recall precisely.

3d) Kasmir Park: Sweeping dunes of yellow-gold sand serve to represent the arid land of Kasmir. In a windowless stone tower at the center of this area is a gold-plated statue of Abn-Kadan, widely regarded as the wealthiest merchant in Kasmir history. At the peak of his power, Abn-Kadan was said to have owned 87 percent of the country of Kasmir. Regrettably, the tower is almost always kept under lock and key; a proscription stipulated by the Kasmirian ambassador and intended to keep thieves from stripping the statue of its gold plating.

3e) Sindar Park: An unusual setting built to resemble the wind-worn mesas and rock spires of Sindar. Here stands a fourteen-foot basalt statue of Nadir Saluu, esteemed collector and inventor of the complex game known as trivarian, favored pastime of the Sindarans. Nadir Saluu's fabulous collection of ancient artifacts is considered a national treasure in Sindar, and is periodically on display at the nearby Museum of Antiquities.

3f) Taz Park: Overgrown with tangled vines, fronds and dendrons, this park was made to resemble the wild junglelands of Taz. The landscape is quite authentic, if perhaps a trifle overdone; the inclusion of poisonous serpents, man-eating plants and other hazards indigenous to Taz, while popular with visiting Thralls, may give less-adventurous tourists cause to consider avoiding this particular attraction. Somewhere in the interior is a lacquered iron statue of Zar, greatest of all Thrall military heroes.

3g) Vardune Park: This splendid park is decorated with terraced gardens, elevated walkways fashioned of woven vines, and myriad forms of plant life. In the central garden stands a towering statue made from a single, living viridia plant, grown and tended by Green Ardua horticulturists for over one hundred years. Appropriately, the statue is a depiction of Viridian; the great magician who, ages ago, created the viridia hybrid, national plant of Vardune.

4) Consulate: A large, two-story structure with quarters and offices for ambassadors and diplomats from each of the Seven Kingdoms. Separate facilities for visiting dignitaries and their entourages are also available. Thralls and Blue Ardua patrol the grounds on a regular basis.

5) Hall of Records: The offices of Cymril's tax collectors, assessors, and related functionaries are found here, as are all records pertaining to tariffs, trade duties, real estate holdings, and so on.

6) Court of the Seven Kingdoms: Seven judges (one from each of the Seven Kingdoms) preside over this court, which handles disputes arising between the member nations. Criminal and civil cases of lesser importance are referred to one of the lower courts (numbering forty-nine in all; seven for each kingdom).

7) College of Law: A university and guildhouse for arbitrators and legislators. Legal representatives from across the Seven Kingdoms and beyond are available for hire at costs of one hundred gold lumens per day, and up. Sindaran litigators, due to their unique mental faculties, usually command fees of up to twice this figure.

8) City Gaol: One of the city's few stone structures, the gaol serves as a place of incarceration for felons, miscreants, and other undesireables. Heavily-armed Thralls serve as guards, with Kasmir locksmiths being employed exclusively as gaolers (all locks used here are of Kasmir make, each device having two to eight separate locking mechanisms). Maximum security facilities are available to house spell casters and members of those races requiring special attention. By Talislantan standards, these facilities are deemed quite tolerable. Still, conditions in the subterranean levels leave something to be desired, or so I am told.

9) Citadel: A fortified installation with facilities for over two hundred Thralls, four hundred Blue Ardua, eighty Greymanes and half as many mangonel lizards. City sentinels utilize the citadel as a barracks, armory, and training camp. Overseeing the entire operation is the commander of the Cymrilian militia, who is usually a Thrall.

10) Sentinel Stations: Each of these two-story outposts is manned by a mixed contingent of Thralls and Blue Ardua, typically twenty in number. Platoons of five sentinels patrol their designated areas in four-hour shifts. If a platoon fails to report on time, alarm gongs are sounded, and additional units will respond. The sentinels are efficient, but tend to be rather humorless, a condition perhaps worthy of note.

11) Palace of the Wizard-King: This is the dwelling place of the wizard-king of Cymril, his family, his retinue of advisors, and his personal guard (forty elite Thrall warriors attired in ceremonial battle armor). The palace is splendid rather than ostentatious, and features a large banquet hall, canopied terraces, balconies, solarium, library, and private chambers of varying size and utility.

12) Council of Kings: A great hall and meeting place of the seven kings, who gather here once every month (seven weeks, in Talislantan chronology) to rule on issues pertaining to the Seven Kingdoms confederation. Facilities for each of the kings, their advisors, and entourage are contained in an adjoining structure.

13) Cymril Bazaar: An open-air market where merchants from across the continent come to offer their wares. Numerous types of goods are available in the shops and stalls, including: seeds, plants and viridian linen from Vardune; weapons and armor from Taz; gossamer and intricate musical instruments from Astar; amber crystals and precious stones from Durne; locks, fetters, and trap mechanisms from Kasmir; alchemical adjuncts and skoryx from Sindar; magical paraphenalia and aquavit from Cymril; and much more. Travelers are advised to keep an eye out for unscrupulous charlatans, who attempt at every given opportunity to foist inefficacious remedies and tonics upon gullible wayfarers. Djaffir merchants, selling beasts of various sorts, usually occupy the southern sector of the bazaar.

14) The Emerald Pentacle: An unusual five-sided structure built of translucent green crystal and furnished with tables and chairs of polished, lemon-yellow glass. The proprietor, one Atherian, was once a magician of some note; an ill-advised wager with a powerful Shaitan is purported to have impelled Atherian to change professions. The Emerald Pentacle is an inn and tavern catering primarily to travelers and magicians. Curtained booths are available for those seeking privacy, a spacious common room and outdoor terrace suiting the needs of individuals inclined to more sociable behavior. The accommodations are first-rate in all respects, and the prices reasonable. House specialties include steamed rock urchin in a sauce of leeks and truffles, Zandir wine, and aquavit of the first order.

15) The Double-Edged Sword: An inn and tavern catering to Thrall warriors, mercenaries, and men-at-arms. The proprietor, a Thrall by the name of Gann, is a veteran who served thirty years in the eastern borderlands and Wilderlands of Zaran. Hearty food and strong drink (Tazian fire-ale, served in red iron mugs), sparsely furnished rooms, and ample stable facilities are available at standard rates. Wrestling (Tazian combat style, with garde) and other contests of a martial nature are held here on a nightly basis. All weapons except garde must be checked at the door, a stipulation suggestive of the nature of the double-edged sword's typical clientele.

16) The River Inn: An inn catering exclusively to Blue and Green Ardua, furnished with tables, lounges, hammocks, and elevated walkways, all fashioned of woven vines. The proprietor, Chachish, is a Green Ardua horticulturist with an extensive knowledge of Talislantan flora. The fare (fermented vinesap, seeds and pods, and giant waterbugs broiled in a savory swamp-sauce) and accommodations (tiered tree-dwellings, situated behind the tavern) are likely to hold little appeal to non-Ardua. A stream flowing through the common room helps sustain the viridia plant decor, and adds a touch of authentic Vardune atmosphere. Prices are about 25 percent above standard rates.

17) Sindar Pavilion: An inn and tavern catering mainly to Sindarans, though also frequented by scholars, antiquarians, and curio dealers. The proprietor is Toran, a Sindaran notable for his collection of rare artifacts, many of which date back to the Forgotten Age. The decor is in the Sindaran style: open-walled, with diaphanous curtains dyed in oranges and deep browns and furnishings of smoothly polished hardwood or stone. In the central common room, Sindarans play trivarian, a game incomprehensible to single-brained creatures. Wagering is often brisk, the players stimulated by rainbow-hued skoryx, served here in spheres of frosted crystal. A collection of one sort or another is usually on display (the demented Sadaan's compilation of skulls and necromantic regalia always draws a sizeable crowd). Aspiring thieves would do well to consider other prey; the Sindarans ward their money satchels with clever devices (many utilizing caustic or toxic alchemical mixtures), and are exceptionally vigilant with regard to their treasured collections. A further concern is Sadaan, who is always in the market for skulls, bones, and other morbid collectibles. Prices are average.

18) Astar Gardens: A nympharium and pleasuredrome built to resemble the sylvan glades and scenic woodland vistas of Astar. An admittance fee of one hundred gold lumens is charged at the entrance; following this, the customer is allowed to partake of succulent fruits and vials of blossom nectar, engage in dalliances or romantic confluxes, and experience the myriad raptures of Astarian culture, as desired. Entertainment is provided by male and female Muses, who project mental panoramas of color and sound for the benefit of the clientele, according to their whims. The proprietor's identity is unknown. Security here is very discreet, and highly effective; six magicians of superior skill guard the premises, their presence unseen until the need arises.

19) The Caravansary: A sprawling tent-complex serving as an inn and tavern, the Caravansary caters to travelers from the Desert Kingdoms of Djaffa, Carantheum, and Kasmir. The atmosphere is casual: customers recline on silken cushions, and are attended to by veiled serving girls bearing trays of honeyed dates, skewers of roasted meat, palm wine, and silver cucurbits of steaming-hot mochan (a dark, stimulating beverage popular throughout the Desert Kingdoms). The proprietor is a retired Dracartan caravan-driver named Nabu-Al Abas. Inside are three large common rooms, numerous small suites, and a half dozen baths. Outside are extensive facilities for the stabling of beasts, with additional areas for wagons and drays. Farad merchants enter the Caravansary at their own risk. Prices are slightly above average.

20) Subterranean Market: An underground market place run by Gnomekin from the kingdom of Durne. Here, Gnomekin merchants sell various types of mushrooms and fungi, fresh rock urchins, precious stones, amber crystal, and other commodities. Wagons headed to and from the subterranean city of Durne by underground roadway are used to convey a variety of trade goods from the Seven Kingdoms and other lands. Gnomekin fare (roots, tubers, and pungent mushroom ale) is available in the grotto tavern, moss-lined nooks serving as the only available style of accommodation. Prices are below average in most cases.

21) Site of the Magical Fair: Situated directly above the subterranean market, this area serves as a public park during all but two weeks out of the year, when Cymril's famous magical fair is held here. The fair offers an incredible variety of attractions: pageants, exhibitions of magical virtuosity, windship races, challenges ("duels" for wagers between rival magicians), oddities, and amusements. Most popular are the numerous small booths and stalls, which offer for sale all manner of magical and alchemical appurtenances: potions, powders, phylacteries, philtres, medicants, tonics, dusts, fragrances, and so forth. The fair is attended by folk from all across the continent, and is an event of paramount importance to the merchants of Cymril.

22) Museum of Antiquities: A monolithic structure over two hundred years old, the Museum of Antiquities contains rare artifacts, many of which date back to the Forgotten Age. Included are exhibits on the ancient civilizations of Elande, Pompados, Sharna, Sursia, Acimera, Phandril, and Xambria. Of special interest to many scholars and antiquarians is an exhibit featuring relics of unknown origin and/or useage. The museum's Sindaran and Cymrilian curators are often available to appraise newly-unearthed artifacts, and may be convinced to finance archaeological expeditions organized by qualified individuals.

23) The Arcanum Society: This is a private club restricted to public use. Members include many of the instructors at the Lyceum Arcanum, scholars of the arcane arts, and a number of prominent wizards and arch-mages of various races and nationalities. The society is said to maintain an excellent library of magical and alchemical writings, plus a collection of rare and potent magical artifacts. The structure is warded against thieves and intruders to such an extent that mere proximity to the building can be dangerous. Admission to the society (as a member or guest) is by invitation only. The society sponsors an annual awards ceremony that is the talk of the Seven Kingdoms.

24) The Lyceum Arcanum: This labyrinthine structure houses what is perhaps Talislanta's foremost institute for the study of magic and alchemy (the Academy of Thaumaturgy in Carantheum is almost as highly rated, despite its less-varied curriculum). Courses are available at Apprentice, Initiate, Adept, and Master levels, with classes offered in such esoteric fields as primary spell casting, magical scripts, alchemical procedures (basic and advanced), summoning rituals, metaphysical doctrines, interdimensional travel, concocting magical mixtures, creation of homonculi, and many more. Tuition is one thousand gold lumens per septemester (seven weeks), or one hundred gold lumens for Cymrilian citizens. Application and placement exams are required prior to acceptance to the Lyceum. Failure to meet accepted standards is considered cause for denial of promotion to the next level, and may, at the instructor's option, result in expulsion.

25) The Library at Cymril: This venerable institution is an adjunct of the Lyceum Arcanum. The library contains over 20,000 tablets, scrolls, and volumes, many quite rare or even unique. The sections on magic, alchemy, ancient history, geography, and languages are especially well-regarded. It is not permissible to borrow research materials except by special arrangement with the Lyceum Arcanum.

26) Cymril Magical Supply: Like the library, this establishment is owned by the Lyceum Arcanum. All sorts of magical and alchemical supplies and paraphenalia are available here, including alchemical apparatus, powdered plant/animal/mineral ingredients, amber crystal containers (various shapes and sizes), magical inks and pigments, parchment, and a host of related materials. The more common types of magical and alchemical mixtures, many concocted by students at the Lyceum, are available here. Raw ingredients and used apparatus are bought from licensed dealers only. Prices vary, but tend to be rather high due to local demand.

27) Alchemist's Shop: This is a small establishment run by three Sindarans. Powders, potions, and mixtures of various sorts are available at close to standard rates. The Sindarans will purchase raw material components from independent sellers, provided the quality of such wares is up to their standards. Unknown mixtures are analyzed here at a cost of ten gold pieces. This is a very reputable establishment, known for fair prices, honest dealing, and quality merchandise.

28) The Magic Sigil: One of the most colorful shops in the city, the Magic Sigil is owned by an eccentric Rahastran wizard named Merdan. Among Merdan's claims: that he is no less than four hundred and eleven years old, the seventh son of the seventh son of the mad wizard Rodinn, and a master magician of the twenty-seventh level. His cadaverous appearance and archaic style of dress would seem to lend credence to the first claim, at the very least.

The shelves lining the walls of this shop are laden with all manner of strange objects: books, phials, curios, scrolls, statuary, sarcophagi, urns, old clothing, jars filled with various anatomical parts preserved in amber-colored fluids, crystals, maps, chests, and a thousand other oddities. Merdan makes no effort to catalogue his wares, nor does he care to spend time discussing matters with customers. Pay the asking price, and the object is yours (no guarantees or refunds). Merdan is equally renowned as a buyer; no questions asked, take his offer or leave it.

29) The Sanctum: Ostensibly a shop dealing in rare books and magical writings, The Sanctum bears a shadowy reputation as an establishment owned, operated, and frequented by black magicians. It is widely believed that contraband substances and stolen goods are bought and sold here, though the author claims no certain knowledge regarding the policies of this establishment or its owners.

30) The Four Winds Travel and Supply Co.: This is a rundown complex of buildings owned by two partners, a Cymrilian magician and a Phantasian dream merchant. One structure houses facilities for the construction and maintenance of windships;

another is a warehouse for storing various ship's components. There is a sizeable docking area, a loading dock for glass miners (see #31), a somewhat weathered lookout tower, and a small, dingy office. In the latter, individuals may make arrangements to buy, lease (10,000 gold lumens per month), or book passage on a windship. Ships depart monthly for such exotic locales as the Sea of Glass (2000 gold lumens, no first class accommodations), Thaecia (3500 gold lumens), Zanth (2500 gold lumens), Dracarta (6250 gold lumens), and Hadj (4000 gold lumens). Passage to other points must be arranged privately; the standard rate is five gold lumens per mile plus a departure fee and retainer of at least five hundred gold lumens. Levitationals are installed here at a reasonable cost, and docking and storage facilities are available at fifty gold lumens per week.

31) Cymril Glass Co.: Situated adjacent to the Four Winds Travel and Supply Co. (see #30), this is a facility for storing, cutting, polishing, and shipping green crystal mined from the Sea of Glass. The glass workers' guild is located on the premises. Ships arrive and depart monthly, off-loading and taking on cargo at the Four Winds' docks.

32) The Four Winds Tavern: This is a tavern and inn catering primarily to windship astrogationists (pilots) and crew members, though windship crafters and glassworkers sometimes come here as well. Not surprisingly, the talk here is largely of windships, atmospheric conditions, and goings-on in foreign lands. The establishment offers good food and drink at nominal prices, overnight accommodations of adequate quality, and private lounges where individuals with a surfeit of money can enjoy a phial of Phantasian dream essence in repose. It is sometimes possible to obtain the services of a qualified astrogationist or levitational engineer by inquiring on the premises. The tavern is owned by the operators of the Four Winds Travel and Supply Co. (see #30).

33) Artisans' District: Here are found numerous small shops, including gemsmiths, ambersmiths, metalsmiths, weaponers, tanners, glass blowers, makers of green dyes, jewelers, furniture builders, potters, weavers, and so forth. Most are reasonably priced, and offer merchandise of good quality.

34) Seraglio's: Seraglio's is an establishment dealing in exotic costumes of all types and cultural origins, owned by a Zandir clothier of the same name. Custom-made apparel is available by arrangement. Prices are high, but the quality of Seraglio's work is unmatched in the Seven Kingdoms.

35) Kasmir Locksmith: Enu Al Muhar owns this establishment, which offers the finest assortment of locking mechanisms in Cymril. Also available are keys made to order (10 gold lumens), custom locks (20 gold lumens and up), a lock-opening service (25 gold lumens on site, 100 + if travel is required), and unusual items such as shackles, cages, booby-trap mechanisms, and so on. Muhar's prices are exorbitant, even for goods of such high quality.

36) Wilderlands Outfitter: This is an immense warehouse and stable complex offering almost anything which an aspiring traveler or caravan master could desire: trained beasts of many types, wagons, drays, rope, tents, weaponry, armor, clothing, and even small punts and skiffs. Prices are within reason, quality is good to excellent. The establishment is owned by a tribe of Djaffir merchant-traders.

37) Talislantan Imports: This is a subsidiary of the Wilderlands Outfitter (see #36), dealing in a wide variety of goods imported from across the continent. Types of commodities available at any given time are subject to supply and demand, and include furnishings, fabrics, exotic hardwoods, spices, scintilla, amber, quaga, delicacies, liquors, and curios of various sorts. Occasionally, Yitek nomads come here to sell items unearthed from the numerous ruins which litter the Wilderlands of Zaran. Prices are high (at least twice the standard rates), and quality is variable.

38) Kasmir Money-Changer: A windowless stone structure resembling a small fortress serves as the office of the Kasmir money-lender, Abn Qua. Here one can exchange foreign currencies (10% surcharge on all transactions of this sort), deposit money or valuables for safekeeping (5% lockbox fee per month), or apply for a loan (25% minimum interest). Contrary to popular opinion, Abn Qua is fair in his dealings, and requires neither the payment of an arm nor a leg for his services.

39) Temple District: In this part of the city are located temples of various cults and denominations. Regrettably the author's knowledge of this sector is limited to the following few notations:

40) Temple of Aa: A temple dedicated to "Aa the Omniscient," stern patron deity of Aaman. It is frequented mainly by members of the Orthodoxist cult on pilgrimages to the east, Aa having few followers in the Seven Kingdoms.

41) Temple of the Ten Thousand: Located (appropriately enough) opposite the Temple of Aa, this is not an actual temple, but a lively tavern and brothel frequented by traveling Zandir Paradoxists. Zandir wine and spicy Zandir dishes are available at fair prices, and the entertainment (Bodor musical troupes, Zandir dancers and Sawilu courtesans, among others) is first rate. The number of individuals who come here seeking enlightenment is sometimes quite astounding; the author, for one, has had to wait on line for up to an hour just to get into the temple.

42) Temple of the Creator: This beneficent deity has a wide and varied following, including many Cymrilians, Ardua, and Sindarans. Services are on high days only.

43) Temple of Terra: This is an underground temple dedicated to the Gnomekin's patron earth deity, the goddess Terra.

44) Eastern Quarter: This is the least attractive sector of the city, being somewhat rundown and poorly maintained. The residents are mainly foreign expatriots and transients; the shops, inexpensive and often of less-than-exemplary quality. The eastern sector is not devoid of interest, as may be attested to by the following entries:

45) Tattoo Parlor: An aged, one-eyed Thrall runs this small shop. Tattoos of the most intricate and colorful sort may be obtained here at a reasonable price (approximately five gold lumens per square inch).

46) Mercenary Contractor: This establishment is owned and operated by Farad procurers, the legality of whose practices has been questioned on more than one occasion. Essentially, the Farad contract the services of mercenaries and other hirelings, and offer these for sale or lease. Their portfolios include Arimite knife-fighters (100 gold lumens per week), Za mercenaries (75 per week), Jhangaran scouts (50 per week), Saurud or Ahazu bodyguards (1000 per month; six month minimum), Vajra engineers (300 per week), Sunra mariners (200 per week), and such unusual hirelings as Green Men symbiotes (250 per month), Mandalan savants (500 per month), and Batrean concubines (1200 per week, 200 per night). Privately, there are those who claim that the Farad also sell slave contracts, an activity banned throughout the Seven Kingdoms.

47) Cymril Mausoleum: A gigantic edifice of dark green crystal, the mausoleum is the final resting place of many Cymrilians. As was the fashion among their Phandre ancestors, the Cymrilians inter their dead in glass: green crystal is the cheapest and most popular (2000 gold lumens, the lighter and more translucent shades costing quite a bit more), while amberglass is favored only by the very wealthy (cost is 20,000 + gold lumens). The departed, encased in solid crystal, are perfectly preserved, and may be viewed by their friends and by untold generations of relatives and descendants.

THE SHADOW REALM

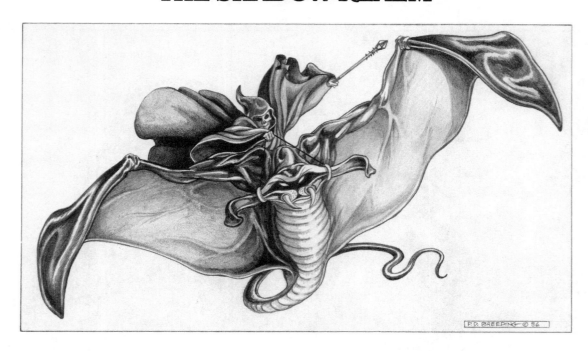

At the northernmost edge of the Wilderlands lies the Shadow Realm, an eerie place haunted by the ghosts of a dozen vanished civilizations. The landscape is correspondingly unpleasant, and consists largely of broken hills, outcroppings of wind-blasted rock, and thickets of stunted tanglewood and thornwood. Shattered ruins, worn beyond recognition by centuries of time, are found throughout the region.

Among the few intelligent beings known to inhabit this forelorn land are Shadow Wizards, spectral entities who hail from the Nightmare Dimension. Comprised of animate darkness, these frightful entities cloak themselves in hooded vestments and bear ebony runestaves studded with crystals of black diamond. Like shadow wights, their eyes burn with a fiery incandescence, and they are insubstantial to the touch.

The Shadow Wizards dwell within the Iron Citadel, a ruined structure of ancient and obscure origins. Its towers have eyes of carved obsidion, which constantly scan the surrounding environs, alert for any intruders who would dare to venture into the Shadow Realm. From within the dark confines of their sanctum, the Shadow Wizards reputedly consort with creatures from the lower planes, such as fantasms, bat mantas, and void monsters.

Because the Shadow Wizards of this region are reclusive by nature, very little is known of their motives. The intrepid sorcerer Kabros claimed to have visited the Shadow Realm on at least one occasion. In Volume Six of his famous "Guide to the Lower Planes," there appears a brief monograph on the subject, recounted here in part:

"I approached the Iron Citadel, heedless of the obsidion orbs which stared at me from the castle's black metal towers. Twin portals of solid iron, each engraved with weird runes and sigils and standing over twenty feet in height, opened slowly as I drew near. A foul wind issued forth, cold and unnatural, as if originating from another world. Summoning the remainder of my resolve, I entered into darkness.

For a time, I groped about blindly, fearing lest I should stumble into some unseen pit or other obstacle. At last my eyes adjusted to the gloom, and I could discern the vague outlines of a long, winding stairway. I ascended and, after a seemingly interminable period of time, emerged into a vast and eerie chamber.

Within, a group of shadowy figures stood occupied at various tasks, apparently oblivious to my presence. Several worked at long tables piled high with tangles of alchemical equipment and tubing, distilling some sort of dark, viscous liquid; others fed malformed imps to caged bat manta, attended steaming vats and cauldrons, or conversed in hushed whispers with winged phantasms. With a pair of tongs, one of the Shadow Wizards brought forth a small creature from the largest of the vats: a hideous humanoid with a bloated head, covered with barbs, horns and sharp protrusions.

An icy terror gripped my soul at the sight of this thing, freshly fashioned from the stuff of which nightmares are made. My mind reeled: this was Fear itself, given tangible form and substance by the black arts of the Shadow Wizards. I fled, unable to bear the scrutiny of those dark eyes, and anxious only to return to the world of light and reason..."

The few brave souls who dare to trespass into this region generally come here to obtain Sardonicus (also known as "bottle-imps"), dimunitive devils which can sometimes be found lurking about the ruins scattered across this region. Much favored by spell casters, who find them to be useful familiars and companions, Sardonicus can command prices of more than a thousand gold lumens apiece. Demons of all sorts consider them especially tasty, a fact which prospective bottle-imp trappers would do well to keep in mind.

SILVANUS

Silvanus is a hilly woodland region located to the west of the Necros River and the Forests of Werewood. Unlike the dreary and fell territories of its eastern neighbor, the wooded glens of Silvanus are scenic and relatively tranquil. Here, fields of meadow grass offer respite from the forest, and cool streams converge amidst thickets of silver-beech, carpets of moss, and quiet ponds.

Among the few folk known to frequent this region are the Sarista, a nomadic race of indistinct origin. They are built along slender proportions and have skin the color of rich topaz, dark eyes and jet black hair. The Sarista are partial to such forms of ornamentation as ear bangles, facial tatooing, and all types of gawdy raiment. The men sport colorful capes, berets, tight-fitting hose, sashes and high boots; the women: all manner of sultry and seductive attire, also of a colorful nature.

The Sarista are a people of diverse qualities. Some are loners who make their living as peddlers, mercenaries or vagabonds. Others, notable for their skill at witchcraft, live in secluded wilderness regions. The majority of these folk are more gregarious in nature, and prefer to travel in loose-knit tribal groups, carrying all that they own in wagons or on the backs of burden beasts. Their caravans roam the western lands from Silvanus to the Seven Kingdoms, stopping in cities and villages along the way. In such places, the Sarista are renowned for their talents as folk healers, fortune tellers and performers— or as mountebanks, charlatans and tricksters, depending upon one's point of view.

The discrepancy of opinion regarding the Sarista may be attributed to their mysterious customs, traditions, and history. The Sarista have their own language, a version of the common Talislan tongue which allows the speaker to convey hidden meanings by the use of subtle gestures and inflections. The tribes do not keep written records of any sort, but rely upon the elder Sarista to raise the tribe's offspring and teach them the secret lore of their people. These studies consist primarily of minor magics, herb lore, local geography and "Sarista culture"; a euphemism held to be roughly equivalent to the less flattering term, "thievery." By age seven, a Sarista child will know every woodland trail in Silvanus by heart, and will have an alarmingly comprehensive understanding of "Sarista culture."

The history of the Sarista tribes consists of a baffling collection of anecdotes, fables and lewd ballads, and has long puzzled scholars. Some believe them to be a people displaced during the time of the Great Disaster; others, citing as evidence the Sarista's propensity for kleptomania, categorize them as the descendants of the countless bandit tribes who once roamed Talislanta in ancient times.

The Sarista religion is similarly mystifying, and revolves around two obscure demi-gods: Fortuna, lovely but fickle goddess of luck, and the grim entity known as Death. The Sarista revere Fortuna, but mock Death, whom they strive to cheat at every opportunity.

The woods of Silvanus are also home to wood whisps, muskront, and other creatures, most of the benign sort. Roots and herbs, many having magical or healing properties, are quite common. Two plants of particular note are found here: whisperweed (which often tells the most astonishing secrets to those patient enough to listen) and needleleaf, an obnoxious, needle-throwing succulent. Though exomorphs and banes from nearby Werewood sometimes infiltrate Silvanus, the greatest danger in this region is posed by wind demons, giant winged carnivores of foul temperament.

In the company of the rogue magician Crystabal, who was himself part Sarista, I traveled through this wooded region enroute to an adventure in the land of Khazad. We stayed for an evening with a Sarista band, who entertained us with their traditional songs and dances. The local cuisine, served with generous flagons of herb-spiced wine, was quite excellent. Afterward, playful Sarista children gathered around, sitting on my lap and giving me gifts of little bouquets of meadow flowers.

At last it came time to put the little ones to bed, though none would go without first giving "old Uncle Tamerlin" (as they insisted upon calling me) a hug. With wide grins, the elder Sarista then brought forth more wine. I listened to a few tall tales told around the campfire before myself retiring. Crystabal, flirting with a charming Sarista girl, attempted to arrange a romantic interlude.

I awoke at daybreak feeling refreshed and well-rested. A slightly bleary-eyed Crystabal joined me after a time, and the two of us saddled up our greymanes and bid farewell to the Sarista. Not five miles down the road I discovered, much to my chagrin, that the contents of my pockets had been picked clean. Muttering under my breath, I cursed the little urchins who had sat upon my lap and showered me with hugs and kisses. Crystabal laughed long and loudly, until he discovered that his purse of gold coins was missing, among other items. With an ill-concealed grin, I consoled him, and we continued on our way.

THE SINKING LAND

The Sinking Land (also known as "The Great Morass") is situated in the furthest northeastern reaches of the Wilderlands of Zaran, just west of the Volcanic Hills and south of the Opal Mountains. The skies above this region are ever dark and grey; the earth below, a vast quagmire of inert, brown sludge. Passage through the Sinking Land is deemed next to impossible, the muddy terrain having a tendency to slowly swallow up creatures or beings who remain stationary for more than a few minutes' time.

A few species of plants and animals have somehow managed to adapt to this bleak and depressing environment, including several varieties of giant fungi, the mud-dwelling snipe and the flat-rooted barge tree. The snipe is an intelligent species of mollusk which possesses the ability to move swiftly through the muddy ground of the Sinking Land as easily as fish swim through water. They are insatiably curious creatures, always eager to exchange bits of news and gossip with other sentient lifeforms. Adventurers who claim to have explored the Sinking Land cite the barge tree as being a great boon to travelers, who can take their rest in the wide, low-lying branches of this peculiar tree in relative security. As barge trees are not securely rooted, they do tend to drift about to some extent, but this is generally only a minor inconvenience. The barge tree also bears a most edible and nutritious fruit, though precautions against parasitic ikshada are, to say the least, advisable. Also found here are the winged reptilians known as Azoryls, and the Ironshrike, a metallic-plumed bird which feeds on ikshada.

It is perhaps possible that no reasonable person would care to enter the Sinking Land were it not for the legends concerning the City of the Four Winds. Once known as the capitol of the ancient kingdom of Elande, the City of the Four Winds is believed to be the last surviving vestige of an advanced and enlightened civilization. It was built by the greatest magicians of Elande's Golden Age, who invested the city with magical properties, allowing its buildings to hover suspended above the ground. According to legend, the city survived the Great Disaster, and still floats somewhere above the Sinking Land, moving slowly on the winds. Travelers who claim to have caught a glimpse of the fabled city describe it as being most enchanting, its wind-worn towers and archways still capable of conjuring up visions of the halcyon age of Elande. The sorcerer Kabros sought and claimed to have found the Lost City. Of his discovery he would only say: "The city of the Four Winds must be believed in order to be seen, and seen in order to be believed."

What riches lie within the City of the Four Winds can only be surmised. Legends hint at the existence of hidden treasure caches containing arcane scrolls, jeweled amulets, and magical talismans. One account puts forth the theory that Elande's artisans created six rare and scintillant colors which never before existed. Another states that Elande's magicians, upon learning that their civilization was doomed to perish in the Great Disaster, imbued a number of "soulstones" with their life essences and memories. It is believed by certain optimistic individuals that anyone who gains possession of one of the soulstones of Elande will acquire all the knowledge of the great magician who created it.

Abandoned for untold centuries, the City of the Four Winds, if it does still exist, may not be entirely devoid of inhabitants. Though it is quite doubtful that any of the Elande or their descendants still live within the floating city, other creatures or beings might conceivably be found to dwell here. Wind demons, shadow wights, and necrophages come to mind as possible candidates for residency, among other, more imaginative choices.

P.D. BREEDING © 86

TAMARANTH

Tamaranth is the eldest and most impressive of Talislanta's woodland regions. Light vegetation and thickets of low-lying trees dominate the perimeters, progressing in stages towards the ever deepening woods of the interior. Here, giant span-oak and fernwood tower above the forest floor, thick with carpets of moss and trailing vines. Swift running streams course through the underbrush, and the woods teem with an abundance of plant and animal life. Two intelligent species of humanoids also live here: the avian Gryphs, and the reclusive Ariane.

Originally the first inhabitants of Tamaranth, the Gryphs are a race of intelligent, winged beings. Standing up to seven feet tall with wingspans in excess of twenty-four feet, they are quite impressive to behold. Their bodies are covered with a thick, feathery down (usually a brilliant red or orange in color), and they have hawk-liké visages and bright, piercing eyes.

Like the birds of prey they resemble, Gryphs are hunters by nature. They have exceptionally keen vision, which enables them to spot even the slightest movement on the ground from great altitudes. The Gryph clans subsist primarily on fresh game, typically large predators and other dangerous beasts. They are skilled in the use of a type of two-pronged spear called the duar and the heavy crossbow, utilizing either sharp or blunt quarrels.

The Gryph clans live in eyries built in the tops of the tallest span-oaks. Their dwellings resemble great bird's nests constructed of tightly woven vines and roofed with canopies of living, leafy boughs. Few stand at altitudes of less than one hundred feet, making access by non-avians a somewhat chancy endeavor. A Gryph settlement may consist of as many as forty eyries, each housing a family of two to eight individuals. The largest settlements often include great "Council Eyries" spanning two or more trees in length and breadth.

The Winged Folk (as the Gryphs are sometimes called) are an independent and strong-willed race who prize freedom above all things. They consider themselves the self-appointed guardians of Tamaranth and the surrounding environs, and are known to patrol far beyond the borders of their own territories. Through their travels and communications with other avian species, the Gryph clans are often aware of events which have transpired in even the most far away places. Although they are territorial by nature, Gryphs will sometimes leave their eyries to travel to distant lands. A rare few have chosen to live amongst men, taking to adventuring for profit or working as mercenary scouts, guides, or bounty hunters. The majority of Gryphs, however, consider such prospects to be only slightly more desirable than contracting a case of gange (also known as "the slow death").

In the north central region of Tamaranth, surrounded on three sides by the purple-hued peaks of the Amethyst Mountains, is a sylvan valley of rare beauty. The woods here exude an ancient magic, as if permeated with the essences of a forgotten age. At the foot of the mountains lies the maze-city of Altan, home of the mystical race of beings known as the Ariane.

Perhaps the oldest of Talislanta's many races, the Ariane are striking in appearance. They have skin the color of onyx, long, snowy-white hair, and grey eyes flecked with sparkling, silvery motes. Tall and slender of build, the Ariane exhibit a grace and serenity approximated only by the enchanting folk of Astar or Thaecia. Their mode of dress is simple but elegant: capes, flowing garments and high boots, all made of spinifax, a silken cloth derived from the flax-bearing pods of the thistledown plant.

The ways of the Ariane, at the very least, may safely be described as eccentric. They are a closed and introspective people, who often appear devoid of emotion or lost in thought, as if dreaming. In truth, the Ariane possess an altogether different view of the world than most of the peoples of Talislanta, being practitioners of the mystic doctrine known as Trans-Ascendancy. Thoroughly incomprehensible to non-Ariane, the study of Trans-Ascendancy enables the Ariane to commune with all things in nature, including animals, plants, and even earth and stone. Masters of the art claim to be able to recall each of their past incarnations; high masters are reputed to be capable of maintaining a single consciousness throughout any number of incarnations, and even pre-determining the precise nature of their next incarnation. As such, it is not unusual to see an Ariane engrossed in silent commune with a bird, a tree or some inanimate object, a somewhat disconcerting sight to the uninitiated.

The Ariane's belief in reincarnation has shaped and affected their culture in many ways. Fearing to do harm to some incarnating lifeform, the Ariane eat only ripened fruits, seeds, and nuts. Ariane tools and utensils are fashioned from stone or dead wood, never from living trees. Even the Maze-City of Altan reflects the curious attitudes of the Ariane, the entire settlement having been fashioned over centuries of time from a single mound of stone. Radiating outward from a central obelisk, each of the city's many unique structures was designed, formed, and polished smooth solely through the use of Trans-Ascendant magics; no tools were employed, lest the spiritforms dwelling within the stone be unduly offended. Furnishings of living vines and boughs decorate the interior of the Ariane's domiciles, each varying in appearance according to the tastes of its owners.

While the Ariane are a non-violent people, they are not averse to the use of force when it comes to defending their lives or lands. In fact, many display a proficiency with the Ariane bow and mace (both non-lethal weapons) which can hardly be attributed to luck. Mounted on swift silvermanes, bands of Ariane regularly patrol the areas around Altan. Unwanted intruders are sternly urged to depart, occasionally encouraged by a fusilade of Ariane arrows. Individuals who commit crimes of a more serious nature are often imprisoned in cages of living wood. The length of interment varies according to the severity of the infraction, the Ariane's somewhat abstract conception of time often tending to add to the duration of such stays. In severe cases, the Ariane reserve the right to kill; the Ariane prefer to think of this as just another way of hastening the natural process of reincarnation.

The majority of the Ariane spend their entire lives in Altan, practicing the mystic disciplines of Trans-Ascendancy and meditating on the mysteries of the natural world. For some, the search for enlightenment takes them beyond the forests of Altan and Tamaranth to distant lands. Such individuals, called Druas (meaning "seekers"), may be encountered almost anywhere in Talislanta. It is the custom of the Druas to return to Altan once every seven years in order to relate what they have seen and learned in their travels. This information is magically inscribed upon globes of polished stone (called Tamar), allowing other Ariane to partake of the Druas' experiences.

Shadowmoon (as he was called by outsiders; the Ariane themselves have no need for names) was one of the Druas. I met him in Sindar of the Seven Kingdoms, in an open-walled tavern frequented by Sindaran curio collectors. My purpose in the tavern was to sell a few minor artifacts, thereby enabling me to finance a voyage to the Eastern Lands. Shadowmoon's motives were less clear, having something to do with "fate," "destiny," or some such esoteric concept. This is the sort of existentialist hocus-pocus which one must get accustomed to when dealing with the Ariane, by the way.

Shadowmoon approached and offered his services as a guide. My luck thus far had been dismal; the Sindarans, with their double-hemisphered mental faculties, had successfully haggled and bargained the most meager prices for my goods. The Druas waved a hand, indicating that he would accept no gold for accompanying me on my journey. I agreed to his offer, overjoyed at the prospect of having saved a few much-needed coins through such an unforeseen coup.

I was soon to learn, however, that there is a reason for everything that an Ariane does. Over the course of the next two years, I would spend more time accompanying Shadowmoon on various missions than in the pursuit of my own original goals. He seemed to know me from the first, while I understood next to nothing of this Druas, who often passed the hours in silent contemplation, staring out across the horizon with unblinking, silver-grey eyes. Still, as time went by, I came to mark him as my closest friend.

Aside from Ariane and Gryphs, travelers delving into the woods of Tamaranth may expect to find a number of unusual plant and animal species. Given its name, the fact that stranglevine should be avoided is likely to come as no surprise. In the evening, the ambulatory shrubs known as violet creepers begin to shamble about, causing dismay to the unwary camper. Fortunately, the adhesive liquid exuded by the yellow stickler is more a nuisance than anything else, though it is certain that wood whisps, imps and other diminutive creatures would disagree with this appraisal.

Beastmen prowl the westernmost outskirts of Tamaranth, providing good target practice for the Gryphs' heavy crossbows. They are dangerous when encountered in numbers, less so in small groups, when they are usually not as difficult to drive off. Under absolutely no condition should one ignore a sighting of exomorph tracks, which may provide the only advance warning of this chameleon-like predator's presence. Assuming that this creature is possessed of mere animal intelligence is a common, and often fatal, error. Lastly, do whatever can be done to elude a gaggle of nag-birds, whose incessant cackling draws the unwanted attentions of a host of unsavory creatures.

THAECIA

Thaecia is an island of rare and splendorous beauty, located off the southwestern coast of the Talislantan continent in the Azure Ocean. Here waterfalls cascade into shaded lagoons, and fields of flowers sway in the warm ocean breezes. Myriad species of song birds, including the rare vari-colored warbler, fill the air with subtle melodic variations. To the west, the enchanting Thaecian Isles curve northward in a graceful arc.

The main island of Thaecia is home to an advanced and prosperous people, known as the Thaecians. Slender and graceful in stature, with silvery complexions and hair a deep blue color, many think the Thaecians to be related in some wise to the Muses of Astar. Though taller and less abstract in nature than the race of Muses, the Thaecians do exhibit certain similar characteristics. They dress in diaphanous robes, and show an aversion to hard work of any sort. The folk of this isle are partial to the nectar of rainbow lotus flowers, a secret distillation of which is used to create "Thaecian nectar," a drink noted for its exotic flavor and exhilarating properties.

The Thaecians live in elaborate pavilions constructed of a translucent fabric called gossamer, artfully stretched over frameworks of silken cords. They build no cities, but simply erect pavilions wherever they wish to live. As such, small "colonies" of Thaecians are scattered across the main island and certain of the smaller isles. The single settlement of noteworthy size is Caprica, site of the "Festival of the Bizarre," an annual exhibition of oddities and diversions attended by peoples from all over Talislanta.

My first attempt at piloting a windship (*Editor's note: See Phantas*) resulted in my having to make an unexpected landing in the vicinity of Caprica. Fortunately, no one was seriously injured, and while the ship was undergoing repairs I had the opportunity to visit the Festival, which happily was in progress at the time of my arrival.

I have seen many strange sights in the course of my travels, but few to compare with the Festival of the Bizarre. To gain entrance, one must be attired in costume or make-up. Wearers of the most outlandish garb are awarded a silver goblet, entitling them to drink for free while at the Festival. Competition for this honor is understandably keen, and produces some truly unbelievable results. While I was in attendance, a trio of Cymrilian contortionists won goblets for appearing in the guise of a tanglewood tree (I will refrain from citing particulars with regard to how this feat was accomplished.)

Multi-colored tents and pavilions litter the festival grounds, each housing some sort of attraction or entertainment: a duel of spell casters for wagers, abominations from the Aberrant Forest in the Wilderlands of Zaran, illusory panoramas, romances, sensations, improbabilities and things defying description. The visitor is invited to observe, partake of, or otherwise experience as he or she desires. Rare delicacies from all over the known world are available, as well as more standard fare, at nominal cost.

The climax of the festival is the awards ceremony, where valuable prizes are given to those who have submitted an attraction or other entry. For the categories "Most Unique," "Most Provocative," and "Most Absurd" the prize is ten thousand gold lumens. The grand category, appropriately entitled "Most Bizarre," carries with it a prize of one hundred thousand gold lumens. A committee of twelve Thaecian enchanters and enchantresses serve as judges, registering varying degrees of approval or disapproval by means of magically exaggerated facial expressions and gestures.

Renowned throughout Talislanta for their hedonistic appetites, the Thaecians are devout pleasure-seekers who enjoy indulging in all manner of stimulating pastimes. The drinking of Thaecian nectar, the consumption of rare delicacies and the pursuit of various romantic confluxes occupy much of the Thaecians' leisure hours. When not relaxing in this manner, each Thaecian practices an art or craft of some sort. Some are weavers of gossamer, while others create scintillant spheres of amberglass called Thaecian Orbs. These items and others the Thaecians sell to traders for substantial prices, or proffer as gifts to the most respected of their people: the unusual and eclectic individuals known as enchanters.

Thaecia's enchanters (and enchantresses) are magicians of extraordinary ability. They are highly regarded for their wondrous images and illusions, which they conjure and imbue within glassine Thaecian orbs. By gently pressing these devices to the forehead, the holder is able to experience unequalled panoramas of color and sound. The Thaecians are also able to store spells within these spheres, which can be released by simply breaking the orb. They are skilled in the making of philtres, powders, rare fragrances, and vivid-colored inks, all of which possess fascinating magical properties.

The Thaecians have no army or navy, and in fact disdain violence, which they consider an unpleasant and over-strenuous form of physical activity. They depend upon their enchanters and enchantresses to protect Thaecia from aggressors, a task that has proven to be well within the capabilities of these potent spell casters. The Thaecians welcome visitors from other lands, but treat the slavers of Imria with a notable lack of tolerance. The two peoples have clashed in the past, for Imria has long coveted the rich resources of the Thaecian Isles. The Thaecians, not inclined to hold grudges, allow the Imrians to stop at Thaecia in order to purchase nectar, gossamer, and other products. None, however, are allowed to stay so much as a single night on any of Thaecia's islands.

THE THAECIAN ISLES

P.D. BREEDING © 86

While in Thaecia, I toured several of the surrounding islands. Although many of the Thaecian Isles are of a size and significance unworthy of prolonged discussion, some few are not without certain interesting characteristics. These are described in the following passages:

Peridia is a small and rocky isle, of little interest save for its massive subterranean grotto, known as Caverncliff. Accessible only by means of an underwater entranceway, the ceilings of this spectacular cavern glitter with encrusted gems and crystals. Climbing the slick and jagged walls is said to be a difficult task, and the presence of lurkers and sea demons has given many adventurers pause to consider another means of attaining affluence.

Dalia is, like so many of Thaecia's islands, a place of scenic and peaceful vistas. Of particular note are a series of bluffs overlooking the ocean and located on the isle's western coast: the view at sunset is said to be unsurpassed anywhere in the known world. The occasional appearance of a neurovore (or "brain leech," as these small, winged parasites are sometimes called) should hardly deter those with an avid appreciation of nature's wonders.

Largest of the Thaecian Isles, **Garganta** is a great and irregular mound of volcanic rock. Here live the gigantic stone beings known as Monoliths, believed to be the oldest creatures in the world. Generally silent and implacable, Monoliths can sometimes be persuaded to reveal a portion of their knowledge, which is said to be quite comprehensive. Normally a period of several days or even weeks is required before a Monolith will deign to respond to any query; less if the Monolith is one of the few demented sorts who are occasioned to acts of violence. As fewer than one in five Monoliths is predisposed to such irrational behavior, the chances of attaining enlightenment at little cost are fairly good. Beware of Wind Demons, however, who come here to mate during certain times of the year.

Cella, on the other hand, is a particularly pleasant place to visit. Nearly as lovely as Dalia, this isle is home to the Thaecian temptress known only as the Enchantress of the Shoals. Reliable reports verify the potency of her magics, which are perhaps the most efficacious in the region. It is said that the Enchantress of the Shoals will grant a wish in return for a favor. The nature of the favor required by the Enchantress is, alas, a matter impossible to determine short of inquiry in person at her manse.

URAG

Urag is a harsh and wind-swept region of arid plains, winding canyons, and sprawling mountain ranges. Once a thriving forest, the area has slowly been reduced to a near wasteland by centuries of neglect and abuse. Its streams are fouled with offal and refuse, its woods felled for timber and fuel, its hills and mountains ravaged by crude mining techniques. The individuals responsible for defiling this land are the bestial humanoid creatures who dwell here, known as the Ur.

Standing between seven and eight feet tall and weighing upwards of five hundred pounds, the Ur are a vile and brutish race. They are quite unpleasant to behold, having leathery hide of a yellow-green color, curved fangs, and facial features of a most unendearing sort: furrowed brows, pointed ears and deep-set black eyes, the pupils of which gleam either white or red. Their torsos are muscular and ape-like, and are often malformed to some degree.

The Ur are a warlike race who rule by force of arms. They ride ogriphants outfitted with crude, spiked armor, and build massive siege engines and catapults. Their warriors wield throwing axes and war clubs made from the mummified claws of yaksha and other predatory species. Necklaces of teeth and bone, pieces of hammered plate armor, and various filthy garments made of fur and hide constitute the typical Ur clansman's wardrobe. Rings of black iron are also favored, and are commonly employed to restrain the hair, which the Ur wear in double or triple top-knots.

The Ur clans have no god, but prostrate themselves before immense stone idols. The nature and origin of these monstrous effigies is unknown, even to the Ur themselves; scholars believe they were built long before the Ur clans settled in Urag. Icons depicting these three-eyed idols are sometimes worn by the Ur's witch doctors, and are said to have magical properties. The witch doctors of these folk are generally regarded as charlatans, most being incapable of performing any but the simplest hoodoos and charms.

A cruel and domineering folk, the Ur clans long ago subjugated the miserable creatures known as Darklings, a wretched race of humanoids who once controlled the region of Urag called the Darklands. The Ur employ the Darkling hordes as low-class infantry and as slave-laborers in their mines and timber-cutting operations. Nocturnal by habit, the Darklings are only minimally effective in either capacity. Of more use to the Ur are the Stryx, a race of humanoid, vulture-like avians. Tenuous allies of the Ur clans, the Stryx serve as scouts, spies and messengers. Some say they associate with the Ur clan armies only because this allows them to scavenge battlefields for carrion, which it is their nature to feed upon.

The Ur clans have three large settlements: Krag, Vodruk, and Grod. All are surrounded by circular stone barricades, and consist primarily of rude hovels made of earth, cracked stone, and rough-cut timbers. These places are havens for disease and filth, and contribute much to the pollution of the local environs. The so-called King of Urag, a particularly huge and ugly member of his race, resides in Krag. His palace, a garish structure made of mud, rock, and a collection of odd trappings pillaged from other peoples, is said to house much stolen treasure. It is heavily guarded by Stryx, Darklings, and chained beasts. Vodruk and Grod are ruled by rival chieftains, each of whom also claims to be King of Urag. Conflicts between the three erstwhile rulers and their disparate factions are common, and often result in bloodshed.

Since their arrival from the Northlands of Narandu, where they were driven out by the armies of the Ice Giants, the Ur clans have succeeded in ravaging much of Urag. They have hunted many animal species into extinction, killing great numbers of creatures for their hides, claws, and meat. The Ur have felled entire woodlands for fuel and timber, and stripped the hills and mountains of ore. Having squandered much of Urag's natural resources, it is known that the Ur clans seek expansion into "fresh" territories such as Arim, the Seven Kingdoms and the Plains of Golarin. To this end, a unification of the three Ur clans is greatly feared by many of the folk of Talislanta.

The Onyx Mountains have proved an effective barrier against the Ur clans, who have found it impossible to transport their massive siege engines across such rugged terrain. Consequently, the Arimite citadel of Akbar, a towering stone fortress which bars access to Arim via the Gorge at Akbar, has long been a target of the Ur and their underlings.

One of the low points of my career occurred when, in order to avoid the attentions of certain over-zealous Ammanian priests, I was forced to take work with an Arimite merchant caravan. We were approaching the citadel, our wagons laden with iron casks of foul-tasting Arimite liquor, when we heard the tolling of a dozen brass gongs: the signal used to warn of an impending attack by the Ur.

Displaying a surprising fleetness afoot, the Arimite merchants abandoned their wagons and dashed into the fortress. I myself barely made it to safety before the citadel's black iron gates slammed shut behind me. Mounting a high tower, I looked to the northeast and saw a mighty, iron-clad host approaching through the gaping chasm which was the Gorge at Akbar. At the lead were hordes of darklings, armed with crude spears and slings; overhead flew squadrons of stryx wielding barbed pole-hooks. Lastly came the massive Ur in their spiked armor, riding ogriphants and dragging giant battering rams, scourges and fire-throwers.

The Arimites let loose with their own catapults, their archers simultaneously unleashing a storm of arrows against the advancing juggernaut. Darklings fell by the score, riven with black-tipped shafts. Panic and confusion surged through their ranks, but the Ur drove them on from behind with their cruel war whips. The Ur catapults, now within range, rained fire upon the citadel, forcing the Arimite archers to seek cover. Given a moment's respite from the Arimite's bowmen, the stryx descended upon us from the skies. My own position on the tower now seemed a bit tenuous, and I retreated to the lower depths of the fortress. There, I viewed the battle through a narrow crenelation.

Though the Arimites fought valiantly, their position seemed bleak. The stryx all but commanded the west wall, and the Ur battering rams were crashing at the citadel gates. The invaders and their allies might indeed have carried the day, but the darklings, in their greed, fell upon the wagons which the merchants had been forced to abandon outside the fortress. Seeing their liquor supply thus imperiled, the Arimites launched a fierce counterattack, driving their enemies back through the gorge and saving the day. During this last phase of the battle, I took advantage of the resultant commotion and departed via an unguarded rear exit.

Aside from the Ur and their underlings, certain other creatures roam the outskirts of Urag. Giant ogronts, mindless herbivores of incredible strength, browse for food along the borders of Golarin. The graceful creatures known as silvermanes sometimes wander over from the Wilderlands of Zaran. The fabled smokk, an odd-looking bird reputed to have an unerring ability for locating precious stones and metals, is found only in certain parts of Urag.

THE UR FORTRESS OF KRAG
(Map supplied by the Jaka hunter, Tane)

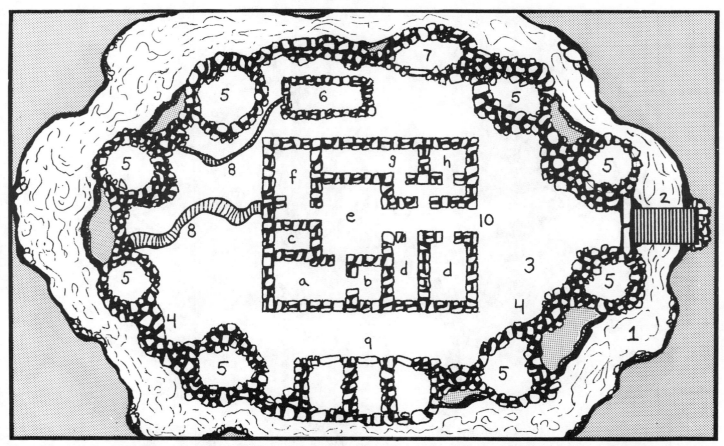

1) Moat: A ditch ten feet deep and about thirty feet wide serves as a deterrent to assaults by scourges and siege towers. The moat is filled with stagnant water, raw sewage and such unsavory creatures as giant scavenger-leeches, poisonous slugs and stinging insects.

2) Drawbridge: This crude wooden contraption is wide enough to accommodate the Ur's siege engines, and can be raised or lowered by means of a winch mechanism.

3) Courtyard: When not in use, the Ur keep their siege engines here.

4) Outer Walls: The walls encircling the settlement are built of rough-hewn stones topped with rows of long iron spikes, and stand just over twenty feet in height.

5) Towers: These thirty-foot structures are used as barracks complexes for the Ur clans' Stryx minions, who serve as lookouts and aerial reconnaissance. A fire-thrower or heavy catapult is mounted atop each tower, and manned by crews of Darklings and Stryx (numbering from eight to twelve individuals).

6) Darkling Barracks: A shabbily-built structure used to house low-class Darkling troops, spies and scouts. Conditions for these minions are abysmally crowded, filthy and devoid of light or ventilation; standard treatment, as far as Darklings are concerned.

7) Slave Pen: An enclosure constructed of ten-foot tall, sharpened stakes, driven into the ground. Prisoners of the Ur are kept here under close watch.

8) Sewage Ditches: Helping to maintain the level of the moat, these ditches serve as the fortress' sewage system.

9) Beast Pen: Similar to the slave pen, only ogriphants and other beasts are maintained here.

10) Clanhouse: This single-story structure, built of rough stone, timber and dried mud, is the dwelling place of the Ur and the king of Krag. Facilities within include:

a) King's Chambers: This king's chamber is decorated with crude furnishings, the heads of former enemies and rivals to the throne (mounted on the walls), and items taken in raids on other settlements.

b) Harem: Female slaves and the least-hideous of the king's Ur wives are kept here.

c) Vault: The king's treasure-horde is stored here.

d) Barracks: Dwelling place of the Ur clansmen and their mates and brood.

e) Great Hall: This cavernous hall serves as a war room, and as a dining hall for the clan's rude feasts.

f) Scullery: Kitchen and storage facilities.

g) Forge: Ur weaponers and armorers work in this area.

h) Armory: Storage for weapons and armaments.

VOLCANIC HILLS

The region known as the Volcanic Hills is one of the most desolate and forelorn sectors of Talislanta. The terrain is torturous, rising and falling in twisted mounds of pitted pumice-stone, angular peaks, and deep ravines. Clouds of smoke and ash, by-products of the area's considerable volcanic activity, blot out the sun for miles around. Streams of molten lava pose hazards to all but the most adroit and wary travelers, and the air reeks of sulphurous fumes. Few living creatures dwell here, and those that do are of a nature akin to the hostile environment which encompasses them.

The dominant species in this region is a race of reptilian humanoids known as the Saurans. Standing up to seven feet in height, they are formidable creatures of warlike aspect. Their skin is tough and scaly, their hands and feet clawed, and their jaws lined with rows of sharp teeth. A primitive folk of limited intelligence, the Saurans nonetheless have adapted well to their surroundings. Utilizing volcanic mounds as natural forges, they make crude armor and weapons, mostly of low-grade red iron alloys. The Sauran clans have domesticated the massive creatures known as land dragons, which they outfit with plates of hammered metal and ride into battle. Though ponderous and slow, these beasts are awesomely strong. The Saurans employ their dragons much in the manner of siege engines, using them to batter down enemy fortifications and as cover against opposing missile fire.

The Sauran tribes live in walled stone enclosures of crude design. A clannish folk, they sometimes war amongst themselves, but are partial to killing Raknids (described further on in the text). The Saurans also have an appetite for man-flesh, and occasionally engage in raids against neighboring Carantheum and Quan. The Kang (mercenary protectors of the Quan) rely on fortifications and heavy catapults when defending against Sauran war-parties, believing frontal assaults against these foes to be tantamount to mass suicide.

The Saurans know nothing of magic, but do have a religion of sorts. Their patron deity is Satha, a fire-breathing dragon-goddess who supposedly gave birth to the Sauran race. The Saurans erect huge cairns of stone in her name, and fill them with offerings of fire gems, a particularly spectacular variety of ruby common to the Volcanic Hills region. Dragon icons fashioned of beaten metal are also in use among some Sauran tribes.

Though noted for their aggressiveness, the true nature of the Sauran race has long been a topic of debate among scholars, some of whom claim that these creatures are not inherently evil. As evidence, they cite certain Sauran tribes who are known to trade fire gems to Djaffir merchants in return for high-quality metal tools and weapons. On occasion, Saurans have lived among men, or fought alongside them as mercenary soldiers. In spite of the apparent weight of evidence, however, few scholars have shown any great enthusiasm for testing their theories by traveling to the Volcanic Hills.

SAURAN ENCAMPMENT

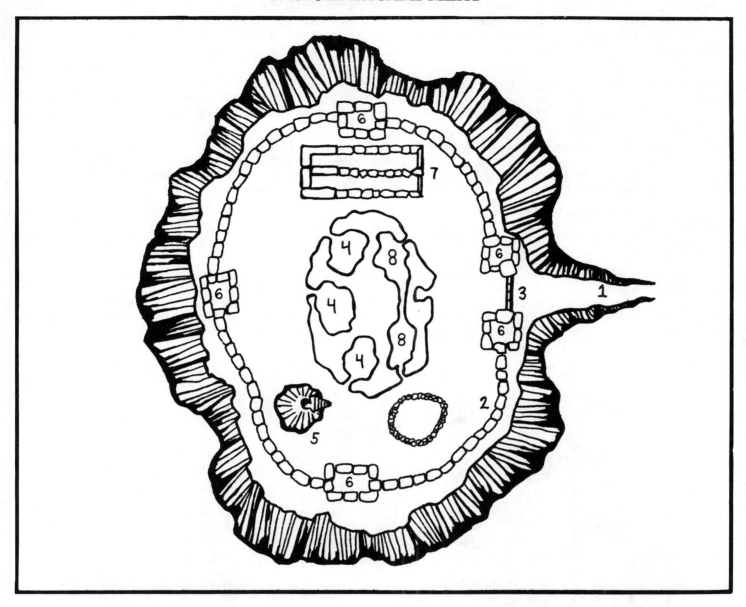

Most Sauran settlements are constructed on top of large, semi-inert volcanic mounds. Aside from affording a better view of the hilly surroundings, the mounds' internal fires provide a source of heat, preventing the cold-blooded Saurans from becoming sluggish during the cool evening hours. Natural fissures in the mound are used as forges, enabling the Saurans to smelt metals for their armor and weapons.

1) Ramp: Sauran settlements always have a single accessway, typically a ramp of stones, dirt and volcanic ash.

2) Walls: The outer walls are constructed of blocks of volcanic stone, fashioned by ladling molten rock into rectangular pits. Land dragons are employed to haul the cooled blocks from their "molds" and hoist them into place.

3) Gates: These are usually made of hammered red iron alloys, timber being scarce in the region.

4) Living Quarters: Caves cut into the upper levels of the volcanic mound serve as dwelling places for the Saurans. The females and hatchlings usually avoid the adult males, who can be unpredictable when hungry.

5) Volcanic Forge: The center of activity in any Sauran encampment is the forge, where the armorers, weaponers and stone-pourers work their respective crafts. Lacking great skill in metallurgy, the Saurans rework metals over and over, attempting to purge impurities from the raw red iron ore found in the Volcanic Hills.

6) Towers: These squat structures are used primarily as emplacements for heavy catapults and as lookout towers.

7) Dragon Pens: The Saurans keep their land dragons in massive enclosures circled by high rock walls. The Sauran females and young are assigned to the feeding and care of these giant creatures, tasks entailing no little degree of risk.

8) Storage Tunnels: The Saurans store their weapons, food, battle gear and equipment in tunnels dug into the sides of the volcanic mound. Iron bars and gratings, secured by chains or crude locking mechanisms, are employed to keep out would-be thieves. Prisoners may also be kept in such places.

Of a more definitive nature are the vile beings known as Raknids. Cold and emotionless creatures, Raknids are a hideous cross between demon and scorpion. Their bodies are segmented, and encased in exoskeletons of tough, irridescent chiton. There are four different types of Raknids: workers (huge, eight-legged monsters practically devoid of intelligence), warriors (humanoid in form, but having tails armed with poisonous stingers), queens (gross, soft-bodied larval creatures), and drones (males whose sole purpose is to fertilize a colony's queen).

Raknid society is regimented and inflexible. Workers build and maintain the massive hive complexes which house the Arach colony. Warriors protect the hive, hunt for food, and exterminate other creatures, thus ensuring the survival of their own species. Each colony has but a single active queen who, fertilized by drones, spawns Raknids of all four types. It is believed that the evil hive-mentality associated with the Raknids stems from these obese and horrid creatures, who are known to exert a powerful influence over their subjects.

Other items of interest in this region include the River of Fire, an ever-flowing torrent of molten lava whose source is the giant volcano, Dragonrock. The river terminates far to the north in most dramatic fashion, in an incredible deluge of flame known as the Firefalls. Quite spectacular when viewed at night, the Firefalls empty into what many claim is a bottomless chasm. Sight-seers should keep one eye peeled for Pyro-Demons, who inhabit the more active volcanoes found in this area.

Not far from here is the Valley of Mist, whose foggy atmosphere is derived from the Firefalls' close proximity to the snows of nearby L'Haan. In this valley can be found the Well of Saints, the sparkling waters of which are reputed to possess miraculous healing properties. Those seeking a miracle should take pains to avoid vorls; insidious creatures of mist, who offer a definite and final cure for all ills.

In certain parts of this region, late at night, can be heard the low rumblings of what would seem to be thunder. According to the Saurans, these sounds issue forth from deep within the Volcanic Hills themselves, where the dragon goddess, Satha, lies. The rumbling noises, the Saurans claim, are the sounds of Satha in labor. In Sauran legend, the Volcanic Hills region is believed to be the birthplace of all Talislantan dragons. While most scholars of the enlightened New Age generally scoff at this belief, few are able to explain the occasional sighting of young dragons emerging from the mouths of volcanos in this region.

Also in the Volcanic Hills, if one is to believe the legends of the Quan and other peoples, are the fabled lost Caves of Erendor. As the stories go, the caves were once home to a sorcerer known as Erendor of Elande. In a vision, Erendor was said to have foreseen the coming of the Great Disaster, and the subsequent destruction of his homeland. Fearing death, the sorcerer made plans to establish a hidden retreat, where he could reside in safety until the threat had subsided. He chose a network of caves located in the Volcanic Hills as his hideaway, and began feverishly to construct a suitable shelter. Working at night in order to avoid detection, he stocked his underground hideaway with all his most cherished possessions: ancient librams, priceless scrolls, rare curios, and provisions enough to last him several years. Finally, he set a number of ingenious traps, designed to keep out unwanted intruders.

This last step proved to be Erendor's undoing, however. In a moment of carelessness, the sorcerer became entangled in one of his own devices. Imprisoned in a trap of his own making, Erendor apparently met a slow and untimely end. His cavern retreat, filled with untold riches, is said to still lie hidden in the Volcanic Hills; a testament to the sorcerer's regrettable lack of mechanical aptitude.

WEREWOOD

Werewood is a dark and tangled forest region situated to the north of Zandu. By day, it is an eerie place: tendrils of grey moss hang from its gnarled and misshapen trees, hovering above thick swards of bracken, toadstools, and molds. Ravens, perched on the limbs of rotting spider-oak trees, assail travelers with pointed remarks and morbid prophecies. Strange shadow-forms prowl the undergrowth, their presence felt more than seen. Other creatures, less withdrawn, wait only for victims to approach within reach of talon, claw, or fang.

It is in the evening hours, however, that the true nature of Werewood is fully revealed. Clouds of mist rise, cold and dank, from the forest floor. From the darkening woods mournful howls issue forth: the baleful cries of Werebeasts on the hunt. Huge and horrid in appearance, these beastial creatures combine the worst attributes of men, apes, and tundra beasts.

Normally nocturnal creatures, werebeasts seldom venture from their caves during the daylight hours. By night, they can no longer control their hunger, and must feed. Only minimally intelligent, they will generally attack anything that moves. In fact, some claim that by remaining perfectly still, it is possible to fool these creatures into believing that one is dead (Werebeasts will not eat carrion). Unfortunately, this theory has long lacked the volunteers necessary for thorough, scientific research.

More sinister than Werebeasts are the creatures known as Banes. Black as polished obsidion, these vile humanoids have pointed fangs and eyes that glow in the dark like burning embers. Banes are vampiric by nature, and feed on warm-blooded prey of all sorts. They possess the uncanny ability to mimic sounds of any sort: voices, animal calls, and even magical spells and incantations. Banes are exceedingly swift, and are capable of moving with great stealth. Their intelligence borders on the diabolical, and it is fortunate that they are few in number.

Perhaps the most unusual denizens of Werewood are the plant creatures known as Mandragores. About three feet in height and vaguely humanoid in form, mandragores stand rooted and immobile throughout the day. During this time they resemble common woodland plants, though it is said that a keen eye can detect otherwise. When darkness falls, they uproot themselves and gather together in groups of up to twenty individuals. Moving silently, the mandragores hunt for prey, which they capture with nets of vines and grasses. Their luckless victims are bound and buried alive. In time, the decomposing bodies fertilize the soil, thereby nourishing the Mandragore population.

Although Werewood is a perilous place, it is not without redeeming qualities. Many useful herb and plant species thrive here, including such rarities as the prophet tree (whose fruit, when eaten, bestows prophetic visions), shrinking violet, tantalus, contrary vine and cleric's cowl. Quaga, a large species of fresh-water mollusk, dwell in the brackish ponds of this region, and are sought after for the rare, violet-colored pearls which many of them produce.

Also found in Werewood are the diminutive creatures known as Weirdlings, or Wish-Gnomes. Bent and gnarled in form, these shrivel-faced humanoids are both odd and eccentric. They are known to amass great fortunes, which they horde in garishly-decorated underground burrows. According to legend, if a Weirdling is caught, it must give over its treasure or grant its captor a wish (hence the name, Wish-Gnome). To demand both treasure and wish, or to cause harm to a Weirdling, is said to invalidate the contract.

Fortune-hunters have long searched Werewood for weirdlings, who sometimes roam about at night, stealing other creatures' valuables and scavenging for lost or buried treasure. Despite their rumpled, almost comical appearance, these creatures are nimble and elusive, and even banes cannot catch them if they have room to maneuver. Locating a Wish-Gnome's burrow is said to be a much more efficient way of capturing these strange little beings, as their lairs seldom have more than a single entrance. Those who seek weirdling lairs are advised to be wary: the creatures jealously guard their treasures and wishes, and often ward their lairs with tricks and traps.

According to the folk of neighboring Zandir, Werewood is also home to the last of the Dhuna, a people who bear some resemblance to the folk of Silvanus. Persecuted for practicing witchcraft, the Dhuna were forced to seek refuge in the forests of Werewood following the Phaedran Cult Wars of ancient times. Some claim they are an evil people, others say they are merely strange. The Dhuna are believed to be practitioners of witchcraft, the womenfolk in particular being credited with having certain extraordinary attributes. Not the least of these is the reputed ability of the Dhuna witchwomen to capture a man's heart with but a single kiss.

There is a single river which runs through Werewood, known as the Sascasm. Flowing south from the Sardonyx Mountains, a branch of the Sascasm winds its way through these forests, disappearing underground just west of the Arim border. At one time, it was the fashion among the wizards of ancient Phaedra to be buried along the banks of the Sascasm. According to the style of the day, the Phaedran wizards made arrangements to be interred in mausoleum-like structures of a most unusual sort. The interior decor of these stone edifices was often made to resemble an elaborate sitting room, dining hall, or bedroom, according to the wizard's preference of leisure-time activities. The mummified body of the late wizard, dressed in lavish garb and propped-up in some appropriate pose, added the finishing touch to the burial chamber. Though Sarista curio-dealers and grave robbers have stripped many of the old Phaedran tombs of their wares, it is probable that a number of these crypts remain undiscovered, overgrown with weeds, vines, and mosses.

I had heard stories of the Phaedran tombs while in the city of Zanth, and had become intrigued with the idea of mounting an expedition into Werewood. Following the fiasco which ensued during our abortive attempt to locate the City of the Dead (*Editor's note: See Khazad*), the magician Crystabal decided to retire for a time from adventuring. Nonplussed by this turn of events, I went on alone to the Zandir border outpost of Zandre, hoping there to secure the services of an able and trustworthy guide.

In Zandre I met Tane, a black-furred Jaka hunter with piercing green eyes and the cold heart of a born mercenary. After considerable negotiation (regarding terms of payment and a split of any profits realized on the venture, among other concerns), the Jaka agreed to undertake the mission. We obtained provisions and gear suitable for the trip and made arrangements with the Zandir scouts to borrow one of their skiffs. Much as I disliked traveling by boat, the Sascasm River afforded us the swiftest and safest means of reaching our objective.

We left the next morning, Tane crouching at the fore with bow drawn, his keen eyes scanning the riverbanks to either side of our vessel. In a state of some agitation I manned the rudder, certain that at any moment the rickety Zandir skiff would spring a leak and send the two of us to a watery grave. The day passed without event, however, and when night fell, each of us took turns on guard so that the other might rest. Tane reported sighting a pair of werebeasts prowling the western bank at the end of his shift, though I saw nothing when it came my time to watch.

Two days passed, each very much like the first, though at one point the Jaka claimed to have caught a glimpse of a Wind Demon flying high above the darkening forest. On the fourth day, Tane spotted something peculiar on the eastern bank of the river. We went ashore to investigate, tethering the skiff to the gnarled roots of a sap-barrel tree.

Tane led the way through the underbrush towards what appeared to be a small hillock covered with mosses, vines and riverplants. When we had approached within a few yards, the outline of a large stone structure became visible beneath the tangled mass of vegetation. Excitement and anticipation gripped us both, and we began searching for an entrance to the tomb. We went in separate directions in order not to waste time; dusk was nearly upon us, and the creatures of the night would soon be emerging from their lairs.

I was examining the south side of the ancient structure, when I heard Tane calling me. Following the sound of his voice, I continued on ahead. Suddenly, a trio of banes sprang forth from the forest. Their purple-black skin and ivory fangs glistened in the dimming light, and their eyes glowed with red malice. Mimicking Tane's voice to perfection, the banes offered sardonic condolences to me and approached with claws extended.

A bowstring twanged from somewhere above, and one of the banes fell with an arrow in its throat. A second turned and met the same fate. I unleashed a Spell of Unending Torment upon the last remaining bane, and the fiend leapt away into the forest, howling in pain.

Above me, Tane stood on the roof of the stone edifice, bow in hand. He motioned for me to climb up and join him, and I ascended to the rooftop, using the tangle of vines as a makeshift rope ladder. There Tane showed me the tomb's sole entrance: a trapdoor of solid stone, to which was affixed a heavy ring of pitted, black iron. Unfortunately, the two of us together could not raise the door, such was its weight. With darkness pressing upon us, we decided to leave Werewood and return to examine our find, perhaps with Crystabal, on another day. The mission had not been entirely fruitless, however; the enterprising Tane had fortunately had the foresight to divest the dead banes of their fangs, claws and certain vital organs, which we later sold to a Sindaran alchemist at a reasonable profit.

THE WILDERLANDS OF ZARAN

From the borders of the Seven Kingdoms to the Volcanic Hills, the vast territories of the Wilderlands of Zaran occupy much of the central sector of Talislanta. Here, amidst the shadow-haunted wastelands, lie the ruins of the long-dead civilizations of the Forgotten Age: Elande, Zaran, Sharna, Xambria, Sursia, Ashann, and others too old to recall. Much of the devastation caused by the Great Disaster took place within this region, which has remained largely unpopulated by civilized peoples since that time.

An ancient thoroughfare runs through the Wilderlands of Zaran, called—appropriately enough—the Wilderlands Road. At one time, the road was paved with hexagonal stones from the Western Empire of Phaedra clear to the fabled Eastern Lands. Most of the stones have long since been scavenged, overgrown with weeds, or worn away by the elements, leaving only a hard-packed dirt trail. In the spring, heavy rains sometimes render sections of the road useless for weeks on end. During other times of the year, the highway is heavily traveled by merchant caravans from the Seven Kingdoms, Zandir traders, Ammanian pilgrims and others, all enroute to Carantheum. Regardless of the time of year, the presence of bandit gangs and predatory beasts makes passage through this region in anything less than a large, well-armed group a foolhardy, and possibly suicidal, endeavor.

While featureless wastelands comprise much of the Wilderlands of Zaran, the area is not without certain points of interest, including the following:

THE ABERRANT FOREST

To the south of the Barrens lies the Aberrant Forest, a weird and grotesque woodland the origins of which may be attributed to a magical mishap of unparalleled proportions. All manner of rare and exotic vegetation can be found in this place, though nothing that grows or lives here is as nature intended it to be. The plants and trees of this region appear heedless of natural law, growing to immense proportions or becoming impossibly gnarled and twisted in form. Murky streams flow uphill, stagnant ponds move slowly across the land, and the very ground seems at times to undulate as if alive. From the underbrush, animate tendrils of tanglewood reach out to ensnare the incautious traveler, hedgerows of serpentine thornwood making swift passage through these woodlands an implausible stratagem. Less easily identifiable types of flora and fauna make known their presence by biting, tripping, speaking in tongues, or through even more unusual methods.

As many varieties of costly herbs grow throughout the Aberrant Forest, visitors to this macabre woodland are not unknown. Alchemists, thaumaturges, and other individuals with an especially avid interest in naturalism sometimes come here, drawn by the region's seemingly endless variety of strange and exotic lifeforms. Indeed, there are living organisms dwelling in the Aberrant Forest which defy classification as either plant or animal, and abominations too hideous or bizarre even to describe.

The profusion of oddities which populate this region might seem to lend a degree of credibility to an old Phaedran legend, which claims that the Forest and its unusual residents are the creations of one Rodinn, better known as the "Mad Wizard." Credited with the development of numerous minor magics and theorisms, Rodinn is believed to have lived during the latter part of what is now known as the Forgotten Age. A benign, if slightly demented, sort of fellow, the Mad Wizard was forced to flee his native land of Pompados after committing a series of indiscretions (reputedly involving the wife and seven daughters of the Emperor of Pompados).

Seeking refuge in the Wilderlands of Zaran, Rodinn constructed a manse deep within a secluded and scenic woodland area, continuing his magical experiments from within the safety of his hideaway. During this time, it is said that Rodinn chanced upon the discovery of quintessence, a substance capable of transmuting the very nature of matter. An unfortunate accident seems to have led to the untimely release of a great quantity of incorrectly distilled quintessence, wreaking havoc upon the surrounding environs. Some say that only Rodinn's swift intervention prevented an even greater and more widespread catastrophe; others theorize that Rodinn's mishap was the catalyst which spawned the Great Disaster and brought about an end to the first and most glorious age of Talislantan civilization. In any case, it was reported that Rodinn and his manse both survived the ordeal, though the Mad Wizard appeared to have kept somewhat of a low profile following this unfortunate turn of events.

THE LABYRINTHS OF SHARNA

To the south of Carantheum stand several maze-like structures of certifiable antiquity. Some scholars attribute these ruins to the Sharna, a long-dead race of whom little is known. Artifacts from the Sharna labyrinths are highly valued as curios and collectibles, if for no discernible reason other than their avowed scarcity. In truth, the Sharna appear to have had an uncommon talent for creating items of the most tasteless and unaesthetic sort. Nevertheless, the demand for these unattractive objects continues to be high in some circles, a behavioral anomaly which has heartened many a generation of antique and curio dealers.

Contributing to the rarity of Sharna artifacts is the presence of nightstalkers, weird creatures who hail from the astral plane. Tall, gaunt, and repellent in appearance, nightstalkers have matted black hide and three glowing eyes. Their membraneous pseudo-wings allow them to glide on the winds, though sustained flight is beyond their capabilities. In the late evening hours, nightstalkers sometimes appear on the material plane, attracted by the dreams of sleeping beasts and men.

The areas about the ruins are populated by Ferrans, rat-faced humanoids of short stature whose bodies are covered with a coat of dirty brown fur. They live in underground tunnel complexes, coming forth in groups to scrounge for food or to rob unwary travelers of their possessions. Ferrans will steal anything that they can carry off and drag into their lairs. They are shrewd and cunning, employing weapons and gear pilfered from other creatures in their raids. Though physically unimposing, Ferrans are able to emit a horrid stench which generally serves to dismay their foes.

81

THE LABYRINTHS OF SHARNA

Pictured to the left are three of the approximately six dozen labyrinths attributed by Talislantan scholars to the ancient peoples of Sharna. The purpose of these structures remains unclear; artifacts unearthed from the ruins range from costumes, utensils and odd furnishings to weapons, crystals, magical paraphenalia and articles of no apparent utility whatever. Of the labyrinths shown here only the spiral maze has ever been explored thoroughly, the other two structures having long been regarded as unsafe.

THE SPIRAL MAZE

Although Yitek tomb robbers stripped the Spiral Maze of the greater part of its contents long ago, Dracartan cryptomancers later discovered many secret passageways, interconnecting tunnels and hidden vaults. Some of these contained valuable artifacts; others were littered with debris and refuse. At one time the entrance was barred by a single stone carved in the image of a beneficent sage. The broken pieces of this statue now litter the entranceway.

THE DIAMOND MAZE

The Diamond Maze has long baffled archaeologists, who first unearthed maps and schematics of this subterranean structure some hundred years ago. The maze itself has never been found; perhaps to no one's great loss, as existing diagrams indicate a proliferation of traps, deadfalls and hazards scattered throughout the labyrinth.

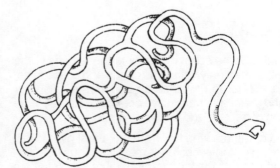

THE SERPENT MAZE

Djaffir merchants first discovered this maze, which is located in a valley surmounted on both sides by towering cliffs. The "head" of the maze is visible above ground, with the remainder of the structure extending below the valley floor. A Djaffir wizard who claimed to have traversed the labyrinth in its entirety inscribed the only known diagram of the Serpent Maze, a rough copy of which is shown here. On the back of the original map are notations indicating the location of various secret doors, pits and devices employed to ward against intrusion by robbers and fortune-seekers. Glyphs and symbols engraved along the entranceway imply that the structure was at one time associated with some obscure necromantic cult or secret society.

THE KHARAKHAN WASTES

To the northeast lie the Kharakhan Wastes, a region despoiled by firestorms and other unnatural phenomena during the time of the Great Disaster. The burnt and blackened ruins of Kharakhan, a city once occupied by a race of demi-giants, stand here like massive tombstones, dismal monuments of a bygone era. Where once flowed mighty rivers, winding chasms now cut across the plains and lowlands. Here, giant land dragons graze on dry grasses, heedless of crag spiders and other noxious predators.

The Kharakhan Wastes are home to the Araq, a hybrid of man and Sauran created by a well-meaning but ill-advised sorcerer whose name has long since been forgotten. The purpose of the experiment seems to have been to breed a race of warriors adapted to harsh, desert and wilderness climes. In this regard, the sorcerer was successful: the Araq's scaly brown hide renders them immune to the effects of Talislanta's twin suns, and their dorsal membranes act as effective regulators of body temperature. They require little food or water to sustain themselves, and can subsist on almost any type of organic materials, including briars and even waste products.

Unfortunately, Araq also combine the worst attributes of their forebears. Like Saurans, Araq are warlike and prone to violence. They are skilled in the use of spears and bone war-axes, but will fight with fang and claw if necessary. From the races of men, the Araq have inherited numerous vices: greed, lust, dishonesty, and a propensity towards fits of unconscionable, cruel and murderous behavior.

The Araq prowl the Kharakhan Wastes in numbers, mounted on the two-headed reptilian creatures known as Duadir. Their primary source of food is the land dragon, from which they derive meat, hide, and bone. The latter two resources are used in the making of many useful items, from boots and loincloths to shields, weapons, and other gear. The Araq prey upon anything that lives, including crag spiders, vermin, and travelers who venture too near their domains. Their wars with certain of the Sauran tribes of the neighboring Volcanic Hills region have at least served the useful purpose of keeping the population of both races in check.

It is natural to suppose that reasonable folk would be averse to traveling in these parts, and for the most part, this is the case. In all candor, however, the giant ruins of Kharakhan are not devoid of interest. Many of the city's towering structures still stand, and oversized artifacts and curios are said to litter the subterranean levels. Of particular interest are the silver coins once employed by the ancient folk of Kharakhan, which measure three to four inches in diameter and weigh up to one pound apiece. Even the most miserly collectors will seldom offer less than a hundred and ten gold lumens for these unique items.

The area bordering the Volcanic Hills is home to a dimunitive species of winged reptiles, known as draconids. Though the bite of these creatures causes searing pain, the Araq consider them a delicacy, and will even risk encounters with Sauran war parties in order to obtain draconids.

THE BARRENS

Westernmost of the Wilderlands territories is the Barrens, a region of rocky hills, salt flats, and wide stretches of scrub plains. Herds of land lizards, valued throughout Talislanta as pack and burden beasts, roam the sparse plains in great numbers. As they are slow moving and dull-witted, these ponderous quadrupeds are fairly easy to capture by employing rope lassoes and a modicum of ingenuity. Herding or otherwise transporting even a single land lizard is often another matter entirely, for the creatures possess a muleish obstinacy sufficient to try the patience of a saint. They are appeased to some extent by salt, which land lizards find most appetizing. Unfortunately, the tendency of these creatures to gather around the salt flats of this region can present complexities with regard to the use of this substance as a lure. Also native to the alkali plains of this sector are mangonel lizards, a combative species of reptile employed as war-steeds by the Thralls of Taz.

The low and craggy hills of this region are riddled with caverns and underground passageways, many the work of Earth Demons. These squat, six-limbed monsters feed on minerals and metal ores, voiding gemstones, which they are unable to digest. The tunnels and caves made by Earth Demons are often littered with these offerings, as well as rock urchins, a species of lichen-eating echnoderms considered a delicacy in many lands. Aspiring gem collectors and gourmands alike are cautioned of the dangers posed by cave bats and the dreaded scarlet sporozoid. The former are great, shaggy-hided creatures of vampiric habit. The scarlet sporozoid has long baffled naturalists, who disagree on whether the insidious organism is a fungus or an animal. These entities prey on living creatures by expelling a cloud of red, spore-like parasites, which devour organic materials at an alarming rate of speed. After dispersing its spores, the "parent" entity dies, and new sporozoids grow from the infested host; a rather gruesome sight, or so some claim.

Also found in the hills of this region are the Enim, a race of cannibalistic, giant devils. They have skin the color of brass, curved horns, and horrid tusk-like fangs. Standing up to fourteen feet in height, Enim are a fearsome sight to behold. They wield huge stone clubs carved with the visages of leering devils in battle, and wear necklaces of skulls, which they collect as mementoes of their grisly conquests.

The Enim are solitary creatures who dwell in caves located deep below the surface. Like all devils, they are the mortal foes of demonkind, and have a special dislike for Earth Demons. Enim are fond of men, however, whom they regard as fine eating. They occasionally emerge from their underground lairs in search of food or amusement. When not motivated by hunger, Enim sometimes entertain themselves by attempting to crush other creatures with large rocks, which they are able to hurl considerable distances. In the rare instances when two or more Enim meet above ground, they will almost always be engaged in such "sport." Enim have a weakness for games of chance or any sort of contest, particularly if wagering is involved. Individuals who have a penchant for high-stakes gambling should be wary of the fact that most Enim know something of magic, and are not averse to cheating if given the opportunity.

THE INDEPENDENT CITY STATES

The Wilderlands of Zaran are populated mainly by wild beasts and savage tribes, though a few bastions of civilization exist in isolated spots throughout the region. Known collectively as the Independent City States, these minor principalities wield little political or economic influence, but serve a useful purpose as safe havens for travelers. The most notable of these are described briefly in the following text.

Maruk is also a walled city, though it is considerably less prosperous than Hadj. Built upon the ruins of an unknown civilization, the city was originally a place of notable splendor. Its people, called the Maruk, made a good living by selling herbs and dried fruit to Carantheum and Faradun.

Soon after construction of the city had been completed, a series of misfortunes, occurring at intervals of thirteen months, beset the Maruk. Crops failed, animals died, the city was plagued by infestations of lice, locusts, rats, weevils, and so forth. Attempts were made to remedy the problem, which was diagnosed variously as being the result of an ancient curse, malicious spirits, ill-aspected stars, sunspots, and a host of even more improbable causes. Time and again, each of the proposed solutions met with failure.

Much to the chagrin of the Maruk, this condition has persisted with regularity to the present day. The city has slowly fallen into ruin, all attempts at effecting much-needed repairs and renovations having long since been deemed unprofitable. Reduced to selling ogront dung in order to make ends meet, the people of Maruk have become morose and gloomy. They dress in unflattering garments made of sack-cloth, and walk about with their eyes downcast. Wan and unhealthy in appearance, the Maruk are considered harbingers of doom in many lands, and are shunned as if they carried the plague.

The ruling council of Maruk, themselves victims of numerous mishaps and misfortunes, continues to seek a solution to the city's woes. Though the government has technically been bankrupt for decades, a reward of one hundred thousand gold lumens continues to be offered to any who can successfully lift the curse. The offer still draws a few optimistic mystics, savants and reputed miracle-workers, though not nearly so many as in years past.

Danuvia is a great stone citadel established long ago by moderate factions who fled the old Phaedran Empire around the time of the Cult Wars. The people who live here, known as the Danuvians, are tall and bronze-skinned, with strong features. Traditionally lacking in any form of ambition, Danuvian males are uniformly feeble, lazy, and addle-brained. As such, the city is governed by females, who serve in all positions of authority.

Danuvia's most saleable commodity is its mercenary army, which is comprised entirely of female archers, lancers, and swordswomen. They decorate their faces with colored pigments and ride greymanes into battle. Equipped with black iron corslets and parrying bracers, the Danuvians are considered among the most skilled fighters on the continent.

Rather than accept their own, pathetic males as mates, most Danuvian females seek male partners from other lands. Each year, the queen of Danuvia holds a great pageant in the city, in which men of all nationalities are invited to compete for the affections of the Danuvian females. The top three contestants are rewarded by being appointed to the queen's "harem" of male consorts, with lesser personages staking claim to the next most desirous males according to their rank or importance in Danuvian society.

Hadj is a walled city, built in the middle of an arid plain which stretches for miles in all directions. The folk who live here, called the Hadjin, are similar in physical stature to the Cymrilians of the Seven Kingdoms. They daub their complexions with colored powders, and dress in layered robes, upwards sweeping caps and long, velveteen gloves. A people of highly refined tastes, the Hadjin wave themselves with scented fans when in the presence of outsiders, whom they deem offensive in terms of appearance and odor.

The Hadjin possess no useful skills to speak of, but are the inheritors of an incredibly vast store of wealth left to them by their early ancestors. The source of this great fortune is a series of giant, obelisk-like structures, built centuries ago to house the Hadjin dead. Over seventy feet in height, most of these megaliths still stand, though some have fallen or now lurch precipitously at odd angles. The Hadjin's crypts contain untold thousands of mummified corpses, each interred with the deceased's most prized possessions.

Located within sight of the city walls, the ruins are closely watched by the Hadjin, who employ mercenaries and trained guard beasts to ward their ancestral burial grounds. Visitors to the city can arrange for a guided tour of the ruins, which costs upwards of two hundred gold lumens, depending upon one's choice of accommodations. Those who crave adventure first-hand can obtain permission to explore the ruins at a cost of one thousand gold lumens per person, per day. Under the terms of the agreement, the Hadjin retain the rights to half of any treasure recovered, along with any and all corpses that may be unearthed. These the Hadjin sell as souvenirs, at prices ranging from two to eight thousand gold lumens.

THE DISPLACED PEOPLES

A number of different peoples and races inhabit or traverse the territories of the Wilderlands. Most are descended from those who survived the Great Disaster, their homelands long abandoned and fallen into ruin. Some are refugees from the Quan Empire; others, members of dying races.

The most common of these include:

The **Bodor** are an amber-skinned people of uncertain origin, round-faced and portly of build. They dress in odd costumes and earn a living by working as traveling musicians. Modest and unassuming by nature, Bodor are content as long as they have work. They are consummate musicians, proficient in such instruments as the gossamer harp, glass flutes and bells, the intricate spiral-horn, and the four-man bellows-pipes. Troupes of Bodor musicians are common throughout the independent city states of the Wilderlands, and may be found in such diverse and far distant lands as Faradun, Rajanistan, Quan, the Seven Kingdoms, and Zandu.

The **Nagra** (also known as "the Jungle People") are a primitive race of humanoids with mottled grey-green skin, smallish black fangs, peaked skulls and eyes like tiny ebon specs. They dress in rude garments made from the furry hides of winged apes, and carry blowguns and long knives made of bone. The Nagra once lived in southern Quan, but were driven into the Wilderlands by forces of the Kang, who hunted them like curs. Those who survived took to living in the jungles of the Topaz Mountains, though a few tribes settled in the Jade Mountains to the east of Rajanistan. The Nagra are skilled hunters and uncannily perceptive trackers; some claim to be able to detect the passage of spirit forms. They are a fierce and violent people, who mark the Chana, Kang and Quan as hated foes. Certain of the tribes have dealings with the Rajans, Farad, and others in the region, who sometimes employ Nagra as scouts and guides.

The **Rahastrans** are the descendants of a race of wizards who once served the rulers of the ancient kingdom of Phandril (the infamous Rodinn, called "the Mad Wizard," may have been one of the Rahastrans; see **History of Talislanta**). Like their ancestors, the Rahastrans are wizards. They dress in cloaks and long coats of blue fustian, and wear pendants of carved amethyst about their necks. Solitary and strange by nature, Rahastrans generally prefer to travel alone. They are skilled in the art of the Zodar, a clever game which utilizes a deck of cards, each marked with a different arcane symbol. While Zodar is thought of mainly as a game of chance, the cards may also be used to divine the future, or to reveal one's deepest thoughts and desires. Consequently, Rahastran wizards are regarded with mixed emotions by most other Talislantans, who are fascinated with the Zodar, yet fearful of the secrets which the cards hold. As such, Rahastran wizards seldom remain in one place for any great length of time.

Sauruds are immense, reptilian humanoids believed by some scholars to have been the progenitors of the race of Saurans, who inhabit the Volanic Hills region. They stand up to eight feet in height, are massively built, and have rough, scaly brown hide. Their features are not unlike a land lizard's in appearance, though their eyes are smaller and more deep-set, and their fangs somewhat less obtrusive. Sauruds favor abbreviated attire, loin clouts and bands of strider or dragon hide usually sufficing to suit their needs. In battle, they wield huge, spiked clubs; partly as a matter of preference, but also because these giant creatures lack the manual dexterity required to utilize more sophisticated weaponry. Sauruds are sometimes employed as bodyguards and sentinels by other peoples, positions for which these ferocious brutes are generally well-suited. Their tiny brains are incapable of grasping any but the least intricate ideas, however, limiting their usefulness even in these capacities. The race seems on the verge of becoming extinct, and there are perhaps only a few hundred Sauruds left on the entire continent.

The **Xambrians** claim to be descended from the folk of Xambria, an ancient kingdom destroyed during the Great Disaster. They resemble the Ariane of Tamaranth in stature, but have bone-white skin and long, raven hair. Their customary mode of dress includes a cape, high boots, vest and tight breeches of black strider's hide, with gauntlets of fine, silver chain mesh. A silver-shod staff and a pair of daggers, crossed at the waist, completes the outfit. The Xambrians blame the demise of their civilization on the sorcerers of ancient Talislanta, and bear a grudge against spell casters in general. Most are wizard hunters by trade, who sell their services for gold. Few in number, they are a grim and moody lot, regarded with suspicion by the majority of Talislantans.

The **Yitek** are a nomadic people, brown-skinned and built along lean and narrow proportions. They dress in veiled head dresses, capes and loose-fitting garments made of woven gauze, grey with the dust of crypts and barrows. The Yitek are tomb-robbers by profession, who range the Wilderlands from the Labyrinths of Sharna to the Kharakhan Wastes, scouring the ruins for valuable treasures and artifacts. They are frequent visitors to the city of Hadj, and are friendly with the Djaffir bandit tribes. Known for their morbid sense of humor, the Yitek are avoided by many folk, who find their line of work distasteful.

The **Za** are a race of nomadic bandits who range far and wide throughout much of the Wilderlands. Claiming descent from the original folk of the vanished kingdom of Zaran, the Za have long contended that the Wilderlands territories are rightfully theirs. In this way they rationalize robbing and killing any who "trespass" in "their" land.

The Za are lean and muscular of build, most standing at or just under six feet in height. Their skin is a pallid yellow in hue, leathery in texture and lined with creases and wrinkles. It is the custom of these folk to shave their skulls, and to forego all but the most abbreviated attire. Necklaces of hammered black iron disks are favored, as are reptile-skin head and arm bands. Males generally wear long, braided mustaches; females, two long braids, one above either ear.

Fierce and cruel by nature, the Za wield jagged-edged blades and bows which utilize barbed arrows. Greymanes, with long manes and tails done in tight braids, serve as steeds for the bandit clans. Though the Za sometimes take prisoners for sale as slaves, they usually put most of their victims to death by the sword, this being thought of as fitting punishment for trespassers. Exceptionally valorous foes are often accorded the dubious honor of being taken alive, so that they may later be slain in ritual fashion. The Za drink the blood of these vanquished enemies from skull-cups, believing that this gives them the strength of their foes.

There is little sense of unity among the Za bandit peoples, whose clans engage in violent clashes over the rights to the best raiding territories. When a clan has lost its leader the group often simply disbands, the surviving members moving on to other clans or becoming mercenary warriors and scouts. It is all the more surprising, then, that the Za clans claim to have a single ruler, known as the Tirshata. According to the Za, the identity of the Tirshata must remain unknown until the time comes for the Za to again reclaim their lost homelands. At the designated hour, say the Za, "'the Tirshata shall be revealed, and the Za will rise up and smite all their enemies, until they alone rule the lands from east to west." Talislantan scholars, who by and large consider the Za to be on an intellectual par with the Wildmen of Yrmania, lend little credence to this folk tale.

Among the most peculiar inhabitants of the Wilderlands are the mysterious individuals known only as the **Wanderers of Ashann**. They stand nearly eight feet in height, and dress in long, billowing robes, which hang loosely upon their angular frames. Their features are entirely concealed beneath elaborate head dresses, and each carries a staff of white oak inscribed with a curious symbol: a staring orb, set in the center of a silver pentacle. Some believe that the Wanderers are without eyes, and can only see by means of these devices, which are magical in nature.

The Wanderers are the last of the Shan, a race whose homeland of Ashann was destroyed during the Great Disaster. Their cities and lands reduced to parched desert, the few surviving Shan became Wanderers, traversing the Wilderlands territories in small groups of two to five individuals. To the present day, the descendants of the Shan refuse to settle in any one area, preferring instead to wander about from place to place as the mood suits them. They are sometimes encountered walking among the rubble of Talislanta's ruined cities, seemingly lost in thought.

According to the Dracartans, whose nomadic ancestors made the acquaintance of the Wanderers many years ago, the Wanderers of Ashann possess uncanny mystic powers. Wild beasts will not turn on them, and even the bloodthirsty Za and Araq tribes give the Wanderers a wide berth. Unaggressive and retiring by nature, they are the only Talislantans who do not fear to travel through Zaran unarmed and on foot.

While the Wanderers of Ashann display a casual disregard for the affairs of other creatures and beings, they are not altogether unapproachable. If questioned directly, a Wanderer will reply, but in the briefest manner possible. They are conversant in many tongues, and know much of what transpires in the Wilderlands of Zaran. Questions regarding the Wanderers themselves are invariably met with silence and a wave of an outstretched hand, a response indicating that the discussion has come to a conclusion.

Ramm, the Thrall who was our guide when I visited Mog, had spent a considerable amount of time in the eastern borderlands of the Seven Kingdoms, which lie adjacent to the Wilderlands of Zaran. Mounted on spiny-skinned Mangonel lizards, he and his mixed band of Thralls and foreign mercenaries had fought against Za bandits, Beastmen and in one instance, a pair of giant Enim. I often tried to coax him into talking of his many escapades while we sat around the campfire late at night, though usually to little avail. Like all Thralls, Ramm was sullen of temperament, and was seldom content unless a good fight was in the making. Crystabal and I both liked him, however; during dull moments, one could always find amusement in trying to count the incredible number of tattooes which covered Ramm's body from head to toe.

XANADAS

Xanadas is an isolated region located high amidst the towering peaks of the Opal Mountains. Like the lands which lie to its north, Xanadas is covered year 'round with deep layers of snow and ice. Atop the highest mountain in the known world (called Mt. Mandu) is the ancient edifice known as the Temple of the Seven Moons. Here, where even the dreaded Ice Giants will not go, dwell the fabled Savants of Xanadas.

The origin of the Temple remains a mystery, its current occupants possibly being Mandalan savants who long ago fled from the Quan Empire. All are old beyond reckoning, their lifespans extended by adherence to certain secret regimens and practices. They dress in long robes of silver and black, and wear elaborate headdresses inscribed with arcane runes, symbols, and sigils.

The Xanadasian Savants are mystics and scholars of unrivaled ability. As the self-appointed chroniclers of Talislantan history, they observe and record phenomena of all sorts: the position of the stars and planets, the delicate fluxes of time and space, the emergence and disappearance of plant and animal species, and so forth. Seated on pedestals of lavender stone, they gaze into crystals of polished blue diamond, monitoring and notating the activities of the continent's civilized peoples. Every event of note is recorded in massive, leather-bound tomes. When filled with information, these books are stored in great underground vaults.

Members of a secret mystic order, the Savants and their ancestors before them have chronicled the history of Talislanta for many centuries. Their reasons for doing so are unclear, but are believed by some to be based on an ancient legend. In the tale, Xanadas, a great mystic after whom the region was later named, is summoned by Death to meet his inevitable end. Though his pupils and associates grieved upon hearing of their master's imminent doom, Xanadas bade them not to worry; he would visit with the gods for a time, after which he would return to the material plane and relate the secrets of the afterlife to all who waited for him.

Those who accept the veracity of this story claim that the Xanadasian Savants are the last of the great mystic's followers. They say that the Savants record important events, believing that their master will wish to know all that has transpired in his absence. Though many think the legend to be somewhat far-fetched, others state that the tale is supported by certain odd traditions observed by the Savants themselves. Specifically, these involve the leaving of a light in each of the Temple's windows by night, the custom of setting one extra place at all meals, and a few other minor eccentricities. When asked the significance of such observances, the Savants merely shrug and cast their eyes heavenward.

The Savants of Xanadas are said to welcome visitors, whom they question at length in order to supplement or verify their observations. They are a curious lot, who seem to want to know everything. It is their practice to allow any who come here to study, and on occasion, some do. Passage to the mountain retreat of the Savants is difficult, however, and fraught with perils both natural and unnatural.

YRMANIA

P.D. BREEDING ©86

Yrmania is an untamed wilderness region which lies to the west of the barren ice fields of Narandu. Hemmed in by mountains along its frigid southern borders, Yrmania features a widely divergent mixture of terrain types: stretches of coniferous forest, rocky hills, solitary peaks, tundra, withering cliffs, ravines, and sink-holes. To the east, the flat expanses of the Lost Sea (described in detail further on in the text) stretch for miles on end. This savage realm is home to two distinct humanoid tribes: the Jaka and the unpredictable Wildmen.

Native to the western hills and forests, the Jaka are a race of intelligent humanoids whose features resemble a cross between man, wolf and panther. They are a striking people, with sleek black fur, a silvery-gray mane, and blazing green eyes. Most stand about six feet in height, a certain lithe muscularity being a common trait of all members of this race.

The Jaka are solitary beings, sullen and introspective in nature. Hunters of predatory beasts by trade, they prey upon werebeasts, yaksha, and other carnivores, selling the hides and fangs of these creatures to merchants in Arim, Zandu and Amman. They are skilled riders, employing lightweight shortbows to good effect from the backs of their mounts (typically, greymanes or snowmanes).

Though considered barbaric by the people of the western lands, the Jaka are a complex and cunning folk. They are canny traders, and possess the keenest senses of all the humanoid races. Unsurpassed as trackers, Jaka are much in demand as scouts, hunters and guides. A few also possess some talent for the taming of wild beasts, an ability which once caused the Jaka's ancestors to be known as "the Beastmasters of the Northern Woods."

While the Jaka are loners at heart, they are known to make steadfast, if not particularly sociable, companions. They are equally famous for turning on those who seek to cross them, and are quite capable of cold-blooded murder if the situation warrants such action.

The sparsely wooded badlands of central Yrmania are home to the strange folk known as the Wildmen. Bestial and ape-like in appearance, the Wildmen have sharp fangs, nostrils like slits, and dark, deep-set eyes. They wear the shaggy hair about their head and face in braids and dreadloks, daubed with various colored pigments. For clothes, the Wildmen employ rude leg-wrappings, arm-wrappings, and loincloths made from strips of animal hide.

As travelers into their territories have found, the Wildmen and Wildwomen of Yrmania are aptly named. They are as vicious as mad dogs, and will attack even large, well-armed parties without the slightest hesitation or provocation. In combat, the Wildmen wield the r'ruh, a sharpened stone blade affixed to a long, leather thong. Swung over the head at great speed, r'ruh emit a "singing" sound which is intended to strike fear in the hearts of the Wildmen's foes. These devices are employed both as hand and missile weapons by the Wildmen, whose crazed style of combat is, frankly speaking, rather strange to behold.

According to the Jaka, the Wildmen of Yrmania revere Manik, a mysterious entity referred to in certain scholarly texts as "The Mad God." Their shamans (both male and female) are said to mate with the hideous creatures known as yaksha, a claim considered to be the height of absurdity in most parts. More widely accepted is the Wildmen's purported use of skullcap, a bone-white variety of parasitic mushroom. Normally a lethal toxin, the mushroom does not seem to harm the Wildmen, who have evidently developed an immunity to the substance's deadly effects.

The ritual consumption of skullcap, a practice believed to be widespread amongst the Wildmen, would seem to explain the occasionally irrational actions of their warriors. Under the influence of this substance, the Wildmen are totally without fear. They appear to be immune to pain, attacking with savage bloodlust even when riddled by scores of wounds. Though considered to be among the most dangerous of antagonists, these barbarous folk are prone to fits of seemingly mindless behavior. In the heat of battle, Wildmen have been known to leap crazily off cliffs or rock ledges, turn upon each other, or simply attack anything in their path (including trees, bushes, and even inanimate objects). Their shamans, few of whom possess any true magical abilities, are said to be even more insane than their unstable tribesmen.

As far as anyone knows, the Wildmen have no settlements, but simply travel about from place to place, stopping when they become tired or bored. Rival clans often fight among each other, a situation which has proved useful in keeping the otherwise prolific Wildmen population within reasonable limits. None of the tribes will enter the Sardonyx Mountains which lie to the south, thinking the jagged peaks to be the teeth of a gigantic earth-monster the Wildmen call Yrman. The Wildmen sometimes launch raids into the Brown Hills, though seldom to any great profit. Mounted on their swift steeds, the Jaka generally keep their distance, harrying the Wildmen with their short bows until the invaders tire of this futile exercise. On occasion, tribes of Wildmen have been known to travel far to the east, where some say they have met with greater success vs the armies of Urag.

Along the eastern borders of Yrmania lies the flat wasteland region known as the Lost Sea. By all accounts this area does indeed appear to be a dried-up seabed, littered with the ancient skeletons of giant sea dragons and other aquatic monsters. Some claim that half-sunken sea vessels of unknown origin can be found in isolated parts of this region, many containing fabulous artifacts and treasures from a lost age. As bands of Wildmen, Darkling hordes and Ur clan war parties sometimes traverse the Lost Sea, adventurers should exercise caution, if not outright discretion, when traveling in these parts. The fearsome nocturnal strangler is reputed to be found here as well, as good a reason as should be needed for not dallying in this region.

I can speak from experience in this regard, having spent some little time exploring the outer reaches of the Lost Sea. The Jaka hunter Tane accompanied me as guide, his initial reluctance to visit the area being offset by a mercenary fondness for gold. Narrow escapes from crazed parties of Wildmen, hunger-maddened tundra beasts and a pair of stryx (who hovered above us like vultures for miles, hoping in vain for some fatal accident to befall our small party) marred the greater part of our journey. Then we came upon the remains of ancient wooden vessel of immense proportions, its hull and part of the prow submersed in rock-hard sediment.

Wielding axes, Tane and I cut away a tangle of petrified coral and barnacles, allowing us access to the ship's cabin. Within we found seacharts and logbooks, so old that they crumbled at the slightest touch. On the floor of the cabin was a skeleton of vaguely humanoid proportions. The tattered and rotting remnants of some sort of elaborate uniform hung loosely on its lifeless frame, a half-corroded blade of odd design still clutched in its bony hand. An attempted mutiny? A clarion call to arms? Or perhaps, a final act of swashbuckling defiance in the face of Death itself? I paused in contemplation of the fate of this archaic sea captain, whose skeletal corpse now conjured forth visions of an heroic past.

The Jaka, who was less inclined towards romanticism, had meanwhile hacked his way into the ship's hold. He returned wearing the wolfish snarl that passed for a grin among those of his race. In his hands was a rusted iron chest filled with coins, all encrusted with green and black oxides. Leading me below deck the Jaka eagerly showed me nine more chests of similar size and countless, worm-eaten wooden crates. Tane then took his axe and hacked off the top of one of the crates, revealing a dozen dust and mud-spattered flasks of aquamarine glass. That evening we sat on deck, counting stacks of gold and silver coins, and drinking wine of exceedingly rare vintage. Never before or since have I so thoroughly enjoyed a stay onboard a sea vessel.

ZANDU

Zandu is a land of gentle hills and sparse woodlands, shifting to deep forests along its northern borders and western coast. To the east lie the Onyx Mountains of Arim; to the south, the sandy shores of the Sea of Sorrow. In the interior region, groves of orange, quince and pomegranate flourish, fed by numerous small tributaries of the Sascasm River.

The people of Zandu, called the Zandir, bear a marked physical resemblance to the Aamanians, both being descended from the copper-skinned Phaedrans. Unlike their drab counterparts in Aaman, however, the Zandir are eccentric and uninhibited in nature. They enhance their features with vividly colored pigments, adorn their hair with silver bands and dress in flamboyant apparel: velvet blouses and trousers, capes of silken brocade, curl-toed boots or slippers, and so forth. The womenfolk of this region practice the quaint custom of hiding their faces behind decorative fans, giving the impression that they are shy and demure. This is hardly the case, as male visitors to Zandu often discover. Zandir men are even less subtle, and in other lands are widely regarded as lechers and philanderers.

Zandu is a land diametrically opposed to Aaman in nearly all respects. For many centuries the two countries waged ceaseless war against each other, until the establishment of "The Great Barrier Wall Treaty" (*Editor's note: See AAMAN for details on this subject*). Relations between Zandu and Aaman, while relatively peaceful, are still far from cordial. The differences between the two cultures remain extreme: where the Aamanians are stern and reserved in nature, the Zandir are fiery and emotional. The Aamanians embrace the strict, mono-theistic tenets of Orthodoxy; the Zandir are Paradoxists, who profess to be mystified by their own existence. The tenets of the Zandir "religion" are perhaps best explained in the Paradoxist text, "The Great Mysteries" (author unknown), a lengthy book filled with over 100,000 questions, and no answers.

Zandu is ruled by a sultan, who wields absolute and unquestioned power over all his subjects. Unlike the Hierophant of Aaman, the Sultan of Zandu is far from celibate. Zandir custom allows males to take as many wives as they can afford, and the Sultan is a very wealthy man. Zandu has no caste system, all Zandir being equally subject to the whims and moods of their ruler, which often run to the extreme.

Like Aaman, Zandu has three large cities. Zir is a naval facility built in response to the Aamanian installation at Arat. It is used now primarily by Zandir freetraders, whose single-masted sailing vessels follow the coastlines as far east as Faradun. Zadian is a fortified citadel built in response to the Aamanian fortress of Andurin. Here the bulk of Zandu's sizeable army is stationed: ontra-riding lancers, archers and swordsmen, covered head to foot in fine chain mail of black iron.

Zanth is the capitol of Zandu, a beautiful city of copper spires, minarets and arched causeways. Like Ammahd, capitol of Aaman, Zanth was once part of the ancient Phaedran city of Badijan. Following the conclusion of the Cult Wars, Badijan was divided in two, and the Great Barrier Wall built to keep the rival factions separated. The Sultan lives in Zanth, in a fabulous palace gilt with silver and gold leaf. Adjacent to this structure is a second palace housing the Sultan's wives, which some claim exceed four thousand in number. Both palaces are attended by countless guards, eunuchs and slaves.

Of great interest in Zanth is the annual Clash of Champions held atop the Great Barrier Wall (*Editor's note: Again, see AAMAN*). The Sultan of Zandu considers this event to be of the utmost importance. Each year he sends forth dozens of his wizardly advisors to scour neighboring lands in search of suitable applicants for the position of champion. Prospective applicants must endure a test of their purported talents in order to be accorded serious consideration for this prestigious post. The eventual champion, chosen by process of elimination, is treated like royalty until the day of the match. It is customary for the Sultan to shower a victorious champion with fabulous riches, fame and glory. Losers rarely survive such contests, a fortunate thing indeed, given the emotional nature of the Sultan.

P.D. BREEDING © 86

Zandir culture is complex and many-faceted. Musicians and artists are well thought of, the best being rewarded by appointment to the Sultan's retinue. Also in this category are the Zandir wizards who serve as seers of the Paradoxist faith (there are no priests or temples of Paradoxy). Elsewhere, Zandir's wizards are largely thought of as frauds and impostors. Nevertheless, the folk of Zandu rely heavily upon the advice of these individuals, as does the Sultan himself. It is little wonder, then, that the Sarista peoples consider the Zandir among the best and most gullible customers for their dubious wares.

Zandir law is harsh in some respects, and lax in others. Treason is punishable by any of an astounding variety of gruesome and slow deaths. Thieves are often exiled, or escorted by Zandir sentinels to the depths of Werewood. The Sultan personally hears all cases during the morning hours, and determines the appropriate punishment for each as the mood suits him. On a good day the Sultan may allow offenders to go free after a brief lecture on morality. On a bad day, the Zandir executioners can have their hands full. Imprisonment in the wretched dungeons of Zanth suffices as punishment in the rare instances where the Sultan can come up with no more creative form of punitive action.

Zandu has strong trade ties with Arim, a major supplier of black iron, copper, and precious stones and metals. The Zandir purchase Aht-ra and other beasts from the Djaffir, and sometimes provide financing and protection for large caravans headed to the Eastern Lands. Exports from Zandu include copper and brass utensils, exotic fragrances, spices, narcotic herbs, fine wines, and opals. Blades made by the Zandir craftsmen are held in high regard throughout the continent, and are also popular trade items.

Of especial importance to the Zandir is the festival known as the "Night of Fools." Held once each year, the Night of Fools is notable for its theme: on this evening only, virtually all of Zandu's laws are temporarily rescinded, and the people allowed to do as they please. From sundown to sunrise the capitol of Zanth is transformed into a veritable madhouse. Dressed up in ludicrous costumes and reeling from the effects of opiated wine (provided free of charge by Zandu's Sultan), the Zandir spend the evening in revelry, debauchery, and mayhem. On the following day, order is restored, and all returns to relative normalcy.

The northern border and coastal regions of Zandu, primarily undeveloped areas, are dotted with stonework towers of varying proportions. Built prior to the fall of the ancient kingdom of Phaedra, these fortified structures once served as wilderness outposts and sanctuaries for traveling Phaedran merchants. Most are now in ruin, or in disrepair due to lack of maintenance. Some few are known to be occupied by solitary spell casters, who find isolation most suitable to their needs, tastes, or habits. The only such facility still in use as a border outpost is Zandre, a fair-sized installation which houses a contingent of Zandir scouts and is frequented by hunters, trappers and traders from the Western Lands.

Upon completion of my travels in the Eastern Lands, I returned to Zandu with the Mandalan Savant, Zen. Here I had hoped to be reunited with all my old traveling companions, but alas, such was not to be. The magician Crystabal was on hand for my arrival in Zanth, for he now maintained a residence on the outskirts of the city. According to him, the rest of my former companions had, through various means, sent word that they could not at this time come to Zandu.

The Sea-Rogue, Orianos, had forwarded his reply in the form of a Zandir merchant vessel. Evidently, he and his pirate band had captured the ship, then released it on condition that the merchants return to Zanth, there to inform Crystabal that (for obvious reasons) he regrettably could not attend the reunion in Zanth.

Ramm, the Thrall mercenary, had dispatched a courier from the eastern borderlands with his reply. Having nothing better to do, he had signed on for another six-year tour of duty with the border patrol. As a gesture of friendship, the Thrall had also sent a gift of five Za bandit scalplocks, items valued as souvenirs among the troops stationed in the borderlands.

The Jaka hunter Tane had come to Zanth to deliver his message in person, accompanied by three ponderous Mogroth. Tane planned to return to the place where he and I had discovered the ancient Phaedran tomb and, with the help of the Mogroth, this time succeed in prying open the mausoleum's great stone portal. Through Crystabal, the Jaka assured me that a fair portion of whatever treasure might be found (minus expenses for travel, equipment, hiring the Mogroth and so on) would be sent to me at the nearest opportunity. Crystabal and I considered the likelihood of this event actually taking place at some time in the foreseeable future to be quite dim, and laughed at the thought of it.

The three of us sat for a time, content to drink Zandir wine from silvered glasses, as was the custom among the wealthier folk of the region. Zen then asked me of my old companion, the Druas known as Shadowmoon. I, too, had been thinking of him, and wondering how he fared. I was about to mumble some vague reply, when Crystabal suddenly clapped a hand to his forehead, as if remembering some forgotten detail.

From a pouch on his belt, the magician brought forth a small parcel, which he said had been carried to Zanth by a band of Djaffir merchants. He gave it to me and I opened it, unsure of what I would find. Inside was a small globe fashioned of violet stone from the Amethyst Mountains of Shadowmoon's homeland. As I held the stone in my hand, it occurred to me that in all my travels I had never visited the Ariane city of Altan. Nor, for that matter, had I ever given thought to the unknown lands which must surely lie beyond the continent of Talislanta.

Zen looked at me, her blue-green eyes seeming to read my deepest thoughts. She said nothing, but only took my hand.

Crystabal appraised the two of us, and shrugged. He raised his glass and drained it at a single swallow.

"To Altan," he said.

THE CITIES OF AMMAHD & ZANTH

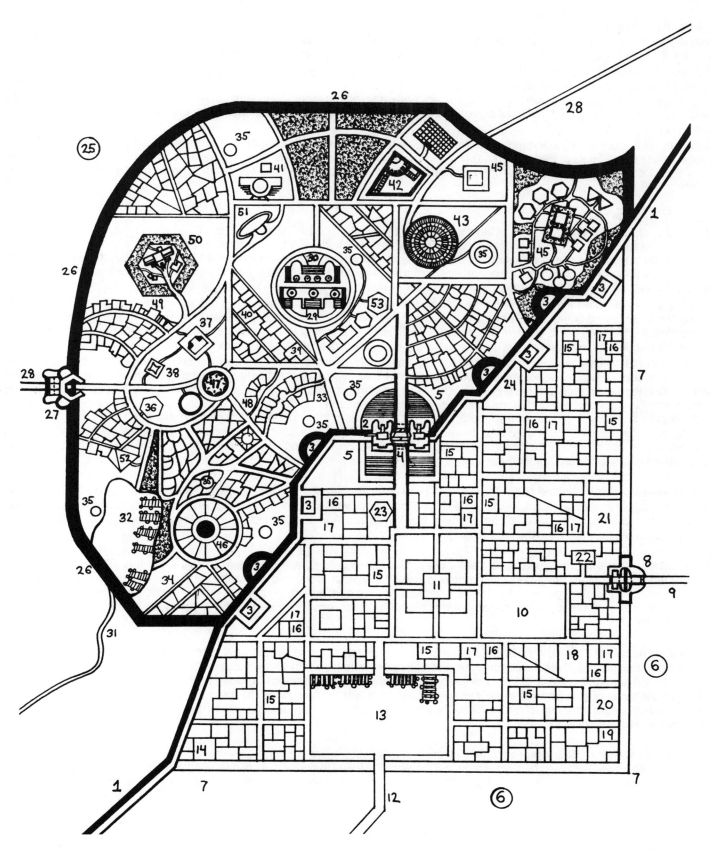

AMMAHD/ZANTH

The cities of Ammahd and Zanth were both built upon the ruins of Badijan, former capitol of the ancient Phaedran dynasty, which was rendered defunct following the infamous Cult Wars of the Early New Age. Aside from their close proximity on the map, the two cities have practically nothing else in common.

THE CITY OF AMMAHD

Ammahd is the capitol of Aaman (*see AAMAN*), and is easily the most monotonous city on the continent. Its architecture consists of a bland compilation of squares and grid patterns, reflecting the unimaginative nature of its builders, the Aamanians.

As is true throughout the country, the influence of the Orthodoxist cult is evident everywhere in the city. Individuality has been thoroughly suppressed: all Aamanians dress alike; they converse in tired cliches, and effect identical mannerisms and behaviorisms. The streets and buildings, constructed of white brick and stone, all look much the same. Travelers from other lands stand out like beacons against this colorless backdrop, and are generally treated as inferiors, tolerated only if their presence is of some advantage to the state.

Aamanian laws are similarly unenlightened. Individuals who commit even the slightest transgression against cult doctrines are dragged away to the Halls of Penance (see #20). At the discretion of the Inquisitors, non-believers may be forcibly converted to the Orthodoxist point of view. Others simply disappear. Accordingly, the city and the surrounding environs remain a low priority for tourists and visitors from other lands.

THE CITY OF ZANTH

Zanth is the capitol of Zandu, and one of the most colorful and exotic cities in Talislanta. From the shining palaces and minarets of the central sector to the slums of Beggars' District and the Sarista ghetto, Zanth is a study in contrasts. The crowded streets and marketplaces teem with a conglomeration of races and professions: Paradoxist seers dressed in brightly colored cassocks, bands of street urchins, Jaka manhunters, Jhangaran mercenaries, Kasmir merchants, blue-robed Causidians, and many others.

The Zandir are an oddly eccentric folk, fond of music, dance, and all manner of stimulating pastimes. Descendants of the Phaedrans, they have retained the unique and diverse ethnicity of their forebears. The populace consists of numerous minority groups and factions, including: the Causidians, formerly a class of law-makers, now employed mainly as legal advisors, diplomats and scribes; the Certaments, a class of professional duelists; the Zann, who effect a deliberate contrariness regarding any issue; and the Serperians, the most respected of the city's many classes of professional beggars.

The city of Zanth, like much of Zandu, is notable for its unusual laws and customs, certain of which seem to fly in the face of any standard concept of logic. For example, there are no restrictions against insobriety, the bearing of arms, or acting in a lewd manner. Boisterous or reckless behavior, fighting, and insulting a woman—on the other hand—are offenses punishable by imprisonment in the wretched dungeons of Zanth (dueling is considered acceptable as long as formal arrangements have been made, and is a common practice throughout the land). Individuals imprisoned in this place may spend days or even weeks awaiting an audience with the sultan, who serves as judge and jury in all such cases. Accused individuals are allowed to hire a Causidian advisor to represent their interests, though arrangements of this sort must be made through the jailors, who customarily charge a healthy "finder's fee" for their services.

1) The Great Barrier Wall: The Great Barrier Wall is sixty feet in height and runs from the mountainous borders of Arim to the Sea of Sorrow. It is built of stone hauled from the Onyx Mountains, with twenty-foot gates, locking mechanisms and ornamentation (plaques, archways, view-ports, and so on) made of black iron. The Arimites supplied much of the raw materials and labor for the project, and profited greatly from the endeavor.

2) Toll Gates: The three toll gates and gatehouses, like the wall itself, are considered neutral territory. The country whose representative wins the annual Clash of Champions is awarded proprietorship of the wall for the year, and is entitled to collect all toll revenues. By mutual agreement, the toll may not exceed one gold lumen per person, animal or conveyance. Both sides take pains to avoid losing revenue when proprietorship of the wall is theirs, posting armed sentinels at regular intervals along the length of the structure.

3) The Watchtowers: Both Aaman and Zandu maintain a number of these structures, each of which measures seventy feet in height and is constructed of black iron (the Aamanians paint their towers with white lacquers; the Zandu use black). Each tower is manned by ten sentinels, whose duty it is to keep a constant watch on the opposing side. Gongs placed within the towers are to be used in the event of an oncoming enemy attack (none has ever been rung since the wall was completed). The sentinels posted in these watchtowers are armed with bows (Zandir) or crossbows (Aamanian), which they use freely upon unauthorized individuals seeking to scale the wall.

4) Site of the Clash of Champions: This elevated, twenty-foot square platform serves as the arena for the annual Clash of Champions. The opponent who falls or is forced off the platform loses the match; if not already dead, the loser usually perishes as a result of the ensuing fall. It is considered a particular coup to cause a vanquished foe to fall amongst his (or her) own supporters.

5) Stadia: These immense structures were built to afford seating for spectators viewing the Clash of champions. Canopied pavilions are available to individuals of importance or position in their respective governments. Vendors hawking food, drink, spyglasses and souvenirs circulate freely amongst the crowds during such events, as do pick-pockets and cut-purses. The stadia go unused throughout the rest of the year.

6) City of Ammahd (entries 6-24): Regrettably, the author's knowledge of the Aamanian capitol remains somewhat limited, a condition attributable in large degree to personal preference. What is known will be herein revealed; the prospective traveler is left to his or her own devices should the forthcoming information fail to suffice his or her particular needs.

7) City Walls: The white stone walls of Ammahd stand nearly thirty feet in height. Aamanian sentinels outfitted in white plate mail (actually, black iron painted with white lacquers) patrol the walls in groups of ten. Their demeanor is typically unfriendly, particularly as regards infidels; a term equivalent in Aaman to foreigner, non-believer, magician, and so on.

8) Gatehouse: The gates to the city are heavily guarded by platoons of Aamanian warrior-priests. Travelers are required to register their names and state their reasons for entering Ammahd. If enroute to Zandu, they must continue on to Zanth without stopping, regardless of prevailing weather conditions or other considerations. Zandir citizens may be turned away or escorted to the border (most avoid possible difficulties by taking the Axis River to Shattra, in Arim, then traveling by road to Zanth).

9) The Phaedran Causeway: An ancient highway dating back to the time of the old Phaedran dynasty. Poorly maintained, the roadway is marginally serviceable at best. At worst, loose stones, unsure footings and flooded sections of road can cause travelers extensive delays.

10) Cemetery: Here are buried the untold thousands of Orthodoxists who died during the Cult Wars.

11) The Hierophant's Tower: An imposing structure standing nearly one hundred feet in height, this tower serves as the dwelling place of the Hierophant, ruler and high-priest of Aaman. The tower's functions are multi-fold: ten heavily guarded vaults contain the country's vast stores of gold, precious artifacts, and treasures (magical, cultural and artistic) confiscated from individuals accused of heresy; four levels are devoted to the scriptorium, which boasts a collection of some thirty thousand books and folios. The upper three levels are for the Hierophant's personal use. Below this are two levels for his bodyguards and attendants, and one level for his advisors. The grounds surrounding the tower are heavily patrolled by Knights of the Theocratic Order.

12) The Aaman Canal: This man-made channel is fed by a tributary of the Axis River, and courses through the city of Ammahd to the Sea of Sorrow. The ancient Phaedrans built the canal some six hundred years ago. The Aamanians, concerned more with spiritual purity than physical realities, have allowed the facility to deteriorate, particularly the intricate system of locks used to modulate the flow of water. The canal is now used primarily by Arimite ore-barges and Aamanian military vessels.

13) Docks: Lowly aspirants and infidels toil here, unloading shipments of black iron ore from Arim. Caravans laden with Arimite ore and precious stones load up and leave here for points east on a weekly basis.

14) Laborers' District: This blandly unattractive area is occupied mainly by low-class laborers and slaves. The latter are kept in walled labor camps, which are little better than prisons.

15) Temples: These temples are dedicated to Aa the Omniscient, the patron deity of the Orthodoxist cult. Each is run by an archimage, who wields control over a retinue of acolytes and devotees. The temples compete for worshippers of high status (whom they hope to lure into the fold in order to solicit greater contributions to the cult) and new converts to the faith. The most powerful temples are sometimes able to strike alliances with factions of the Knights of the Theocratic Order, thereby attaining an even greater degree of influence.

16) Towers of the Monitors: These fifty-foot stone towers serve as the dwelling places of Ammahd's monitors, each of whom serves as the ruling prelate of his or her assigned district. The number and wealth of a district's temples, the status of its archimages, and the extent of its influence with the Knights of the Theocratic Order are all factors contributing to the monitor's prestige and status. Consequently, competition between the monitors—who are constantly scrutinized by representatives of the Hierophant—is often fierce. Individuals hoping to verify increases in mana must file claims with the monitor assigned to their district. Adjudicators serving the monitor process all such claims, with results being posted outside the tower gates on the following day.

17) Monasteries: Sequestered within these fortified structures are the various factions of the Knights of the Theocratic Order. Each is a military enclave specializing in a single area of expertise, such as: naval operations, cavalry, infantry, Inquisitors (see #20), witch hunters, sentinels, border patrol, and so on. The facilities available in the monasteries vary in type and quality according to the degree of influence wielded by that particular faction; though all warrior-priests of the order are sworn to obey the dictates of the Hierophant, the various factions typically vie with one another for new recruits, and for contributions from temples seeking to gain the Knights' allegiance.

18) Reliquary: This is a museum of artifacts purported to have great significance to members of the Orthodoxist cult: the soiled garments of an Orthodoxist seer, the personal effects of martyrs to the cult, the bones of purported saints, and so forth. The majority of these items were dredged from ancient ruins and holy sites by pilgrims of the faith. A donation of ten gold lumens is charged for admittance.

19) Depiliator: This is a facility where cultists come for the ritual removal of facial and bodily hair, a process accomplished through immersion in vats filled with the foul-smelling juice of the bald-nettle plant; the first of many ritual observances which new converts to the cult must undergo. The depiliators (usually males over the age of seventy) customarily wear blindfolds while engaged in their work. A donation of five gold lumens is required.

20) Halls of Penance: Here, newly depiliated converts and individuals accused of impropriety are absolved of their sins. The methods employed vary greatly, and include dunking (in deep wells), flogging, beating with wooden staves, and more unusual forms of physical and psychological punishment. The Inquisitors (warrior-priests assigned to the Halls of Penance) are quite creative, particularly as regards the extraction of confessions from tight-lipped sinners and heretics. In the lower levels are dungeon cells for the benefit of those recalcitrants who are deemed to require a more prolonged form of absolution.

21) Pilgrimage Supply: This immense establishment (technically owned by the Hierophant) offers all that an individual undertaking a pilgrimage or crusade of some sort could possible desire: cult-approved travelers' raiment, maps, wagons, burden beasts, dray beasts, slave bearers, rations, cult holy items, and a host of sundries and assorted goods. A trio of archimages manages the operation. Costs are at least 50% above average.

22) The Pilgrim's Rest: This is an inn catering to pilgrims of the Orthodoxist cult, many of whom come to visit Ammahd from the Aamanian cities of Arat and Andurin. The inn's fare is notably devoid of flavor or spice. Alcoholic beverages and musical entertainment are prohibited, and costs are somewhat above average.

23) Hall of Meditation: Here, members of the Orthodoxist cult can gather together with their peers to meditate, discuss the doctrines of Orthodoxy, or read the latest decrees of the Hierophant. Scribes are on hand to copy new edicts from the Omnival as needed.

24) Mercantilers District: In this section of the city are many small shops and establishments, including limners (selling white lacquers), clothiers (cult vestments only), tanners, millers, masons, carpenters, potters and so forth. None will dare sell any wares which have not been approved by the Orthodoxist cult.

25) City of Zanth (entries 25-53): The capitol of Zandu is, by contrast, a wonderfully colorful and enticing place. Points of interest include the following:

26) City Walls: The black stone walls of Zanth stand about thirty feet in height. Zandir sentinels, outfitted in black iron chain mail, patrol the walls in platoons of ten to twelve individuals (both males and females serve in the Zandir military). Most are friendly, some perhaps overtly so; the Zandir are prone to excess, and notably lacking in restraint as pertains to relations with members of the opposite sex.

27) Gatehouse: Contingents of twenty sentinels guard the gates to the city. Spot checks of suspicious-looking individuals and cargoes occur from time to time. In return for the treatment accorded Zandir citizens at the border of Aaman, Aamanians who attempt to pass this way are routinely turned away.

28) The Phaedran Causeway: This is the western extension of the ancient roadway described at #9, with pretty much the same problems. The northern extension, heading into Arim, is better-maintained (thanks to the Arimites), though still not entirely free of difficulties: ice and snow in the winter months, fierce Drukh war-parties, and predatory beasts, to name a few.

29) The Sultan's Palace: A fabulous structure gilt in silver and gold leaf, reminiscent of the storied architecture of ancient Badijan. The grounds are decorated with canopied terraces, fountains, walkways and topiary gardens. The interior boasts lavish accoutrements such as plush Zandir carpets, aviaries, solariums, cushioned divans, spiral stairways, and a vast collection of paintings, sculptures, and tapestries. Here, the Sultan of Zandu dwells amidst great splendor, attended by his hosts of servitors, astromancers, viziers and his personal corps of elite swordsmen and swordswomen (see #41 and 42).

30) Palace of the Sultan's Harem: Situated adjacent to the Sultan's own palace, this marvelous structure houses the grand potentate's four thousand-odd wives, plus half again as many eunuchs, hand maidens and servants. Several hundred of the Sultan's offspring are tended to in a connecting nursery.

31) The Zandu Canal: This man-made channel runs south to the Sea of Sorrow. Built long ago by the ancient Phaedrans, it has been maintained with less than exceptional dedication. The canal is used by Zandir freetraders, the Zandir navy, and the Sultan's pleasure craft.

32) Docks: Zandir freetraders disembark from this point, carrying shipments of spices, copper and brass articles, fine Zandir blades and other goods to such places as the Thaecian Isles, Jhangara, Faradun, and the Zandir cities of Zadian and Zir.

33) The Marketplace: A colorful bazaar frequented by buyers and sellers from many lands: Gnomekin crystal merchants from Durne, Ardua horticulturists, Kasmir trapsmiths, Cymrilian potion-dealers, Farad slave mongers and procurers, Sarista fortune-tellers, Jaka trappers, Zandir spice traders, Arimite ore and gem dealers, and others. Many of the shops and stalls located here remain open far into the night, when the marketplace, ablaze with torchlight, is most active.

34) Beggars' District: This rundown section of the city is inhabited by the lower echelons of Zanth society, the majority of whom earn a living as beggars (in Zandu, begging is considered an honest, if not particularly estimable, profession). It is the custom of the Zandir to scatter handfuls of copper coins about when accosted by beggars, both as a sign of generosity and to keep from being further harassed. Individuals who fail to adhere to this custom, whether through ignorance or miserliness, may expect to be subjected to public scorn and ridicule; though many of the inhabitants of the Beggars' District are thieves, cut-throats or outright fakers, the Zandir are fond of their beggars, and expect others to be equally open-minded.

35) Sentinel Towers: These three-story structures are utilized by platoons of Zandir swordsmen and swordswomen (typically twenty in number), outfitted in fine, black iron chain mail. The reliability of these units, given the Zandir penchant for romantic pursuits, is often suspect. Their skill, however, is not; only a fool would cross swords with these highly-trained fighters.

36) The Zandu Baths: An exotic establishment popular with many of the folk of Zanth, the baths offer refreshment (Zandir wine and sweetmeats), lavation, and stimulating conversation. Private baths, with or without an accompanying masseuse, are available on request. Prices are average, and the quality of service is exemplary.

37) Manse of the Sublime Mysteries: A splendid inn and tavern decorated in the eccentric style of the ancient Phaedrans, who were enamored of colorful pavilions, diaphanous curtains, and velvet furnishings. It is required of all who enter this place to wear a mask of one sort or another, a curious custom which adds an air of mystery and suspense to the proceedings. Entertainment is provided by troupes of Bodor musicians, actors, jongleurs, or daredevils, according to the schedule. Prices are well above average, though not excessive given the unique nature of the experience.

38) The House of Chance: This is a rather lavish establishment catering to individuals with a penchant for gambling. The rogue magician Crystabal, who falls neatly into this category, wholeheartedly endorses the many attractions and diversions offered within. The author, having an aversion to the easy loss of hard-earned lumens, has long upheld the practice of avoiding places such as this, where one can find individuals willing to lay odds on just about any game or activity imaginable.

39) Costumer: A shop specializing in masks, elaborate costumes, and other fanciful apparel. Made-to-order outfits are available at double the usual prices, which in any event are not cheap. Body-painting (with colored pigments) is also available, at costs ranging from twenty to two hundred gold lumens.

40) Bladesmith: The largest and most prestigious such shop in Zandu, owned and operated by the same family of Zandir craftsmen for many generations. Over a hundred bladesmiths and armorers work here, filling orders from across the continent. Prices are twice the standard rates (three times standard rates for custom-made items), but the quality of the workmanship is beyond compare.

41) Zandu School of Swordsmanship: The most renowned martial institute in the country, the Zandu school offers private instruction in the famed Zandir sword-fighting style. Courses are available at all levels, from beginner to master status. Tuition is two hundred gold lumens per septemester (half this for Zandir citizens). Individuals who wish to serve in any branch of the Zandu military must first earn a degree from this unique school.

42) The Citadel at Zanth: This fortified structure serves as the base of operations for the six branches of the Zandu military: Greymane cavalry, sea patrol, border scouts, city sentinels, armored infantry and elite guardsmen. Each branch has its own barracks complex, center for operations, and general staff. Members of the Zandir military are essentially treated as mercenaries; only trained swordsmen and swordswomen can apply for duty, with qualified individuals being hired on a yearly basis. The pay is good: one hundred gold lumens per week, to start.

43) Arena of Champions: This is a large arena where battles between armed contestants are held once each week. The purpose of the competition is to decide who will represent Zandu at the annual Clash of Champions. A series of bouts is scheduled, the champion being determined by process of elimination. The competition is open to warriors of any race, creed or nationality, and offers a chance for gold and glory: each victory in the arena is worth a thousand gold lumens, and the champion is accorded status commensurate with a prince of the realm by the Sultan himself. Seats are available to spectators at a cost of one, ten, or one hundred gold lumens.

44) The Dungeons of Zanth: An archaic facility which dates back to the time of the Phaedran dynasty, the dungeons of Zanth serve as a place of incarceration, torture and execution. The structure stands only three stories in height, but extends some seven stories below the ground. Rumors regarding the dungeons are numerous: some say the structure is riddled with narrow tunnels and passageways, created by prisoners attempting to dig their way to freedom. Others claim that parts of the lower levels were sealed off over a hundred years ago; that unspeakable acts were performed therein; and that ancient Phaedran wizards lie entombed in the subterranean depths.

45) The Zandu Menagerie: This is a zoo and park area open to the general public. Wild beasts of many sorts are kept here, including a number of rare and nearly extinct species. Of special interest is a cage holding the only known pair of Mendaxites, a species of smallish humanoids genetically incapable of telling the truth. Admission is one silver piece. The menagerie's owner, a Zandir scholar named Armitas, will purchase healthy specimens of rare or unusual creatures from reputable sellers.

46) Sarista Ghetto: Formerly a public park, this area has been taken over by wandering Sarista gypsy clans from the western woodlands of Silvanus. Wagons and baggage trains are scattered throughout the area, the Sarista population alternately shrinking or growing with the arrival and departure of new clans. The Zandu government grudgingly tolerates the presence of the Sarista, who are generally quite popular among the citizens of Zanth. Many Zandir come here to have their fortunes told, or to consort with the uninhibited Sarista men and womenfolk.

47) Institute of Paradoxy: Erstwhile center for the study of Paradoxy, the institute is perhaps best described as a school for magicians, charlatans and self-styled seers. The curriculum and faculty are hopelessly disorganized, with the result that individuals graduating from the institute may or may not actually have attained any appreciable magical abilities. Tuition is one hundred gold lumens per septemester (seven weeks), half this for Zandir citizens.

48) The Mystic Circle: This is a shop specializing in Paradoxist literature (including copies of the curious cult manifesto, "The Great Mysteries"), magical paraphenalia and alchemical ingredients. Scilla the Hylomancer, an aging Zandir crone with reputed psychic powers, owns this establishment. She receives regular shipments of herbs and animal ingredients from a Dhuna warlock, who purportedly makes his home in the depths of Werewood. Prices vary, as does the quality of merchandise offered here.

49) Zandu Properties: A wealthy Zandir merchant owns this establishment, which sells parcels of land, refurbished manses, and abandoned tower keeps. Most of these properties are situated amidst the northern border and coastal regions of Zandu; not exactly the most preferred locations, though the relatively low prices (five-to-fifty thousand gold lumens, on the average) are not unappealing, particularly to individuals on a limited budget.

50) Vineyard/Winery: This is one of the country's most respected wineries, offering excellent vintage wines at reasonable cost. Weekly tours of the vineyards, costing one silver piece per person, are a popular attraction, and contribute greatly to the general lack of sobriety exhibited by people in these parts.

51) Crematorium/Mausoleum: Here, interred in brass urns, are the ashes of the untold thousands of Paradoxists who died during the Cult Wars of ancient times. The facility is still in use.

52) The Werewood Tavern: This is an inn and tavern frequented by a truly diverse clientele: Arimite knife-fighters, Jaka manhunters, Zandir border scouts, wizards, mountebanks and thieves. The fare is plain but hardy, and reasonably priced. In the large common room are held such entertaining spectacles as knife-throwing contests, exhibitions of magic, and tests of strength and skill. The private booths are quite popular with certain of the tavern's more disreputable customers, who are said to use the facilities as offices for the sale and distribution of contraband, stolen merchandise and various illicit wares. All in all, there is seldom a dull moment at this unusual night-spot.

53) Causidians' Guild: This is a meeting place and guildhouse for Zanth's considerable population of Causidians, whose services may be obtained for a price of fifty gold lumens per day; more, if the Causidian has garnered even the slightest reputation.

APPENDIX

The following appendices were compiled from the notes of the wizard, Tamerlin. For the benefit of the reader, a guide to the pronunciation of Talislantan names and places has been included at the end of this book. As the only available source of reference was Tamerlin's chronicles, the accuracy and reliability of this guide may indeed be moot issues.

THE UNKNOWN LANDS

In addition to the many strange and wondrous places described in the preceding text, a number of legends hint at the existence of lands rumored to lie far to the east and west of the Talislantan continent. As yet unexplored by the folk of Talislanta, who for the most part have a superstitious aversion to the open sea, these Unknown Lands present fertile ground for the aspiring explorer. What little is known of these places shall be related to the reader, though the veracity of these accounts is currently beyond the author's ability to ascertain. Gods willing, a voyage to one or more of the Unknown Lands may lie in my own future. In truth, however, the author has somewhat less of a liking for sailing ships and uncharted waters than the average Talislantan.

THE MIDNIGHT REALM: Beyond the Midnight Sea is said to lie the Midnight Realm, a region where darkness ever prevails over light. This, some say, is the home of the Night Demons, who dwell in towers of black basalt. Their ruler, who is called the Lord of the Night Skies, is rumored to be a wealthy and powerful necromancer. Rivers of molten iron are said to run across the land, emptying into the dark waters of the Midnight Sea in a torrent of slag and steam. The nature of the tales concerning the Midnight Realm is such that it is little wonder that few have ever shown any marked desire to explore this region.

SIMBAR: A legend much in favor with the folk of Quan describes the land of Simbar, which lies "far to the northeast, where the Sea of Madness gives way to the peaceful blue waters of the Sea of Serenity." According to the Quan, Simbar is "a splendid land, whose people live in ruby-colored castles, and sail the seas in crystal ships." The ancient Phaedran scholars, being somewhat less optimistic, described Simbar as home to "the ruins of a once-glorious, but now faded, civilization. The ghosts of its long-dead population still haunt Simbar's cities, jealously guarding those things which they once held so dear in their hearts: namely, chests of silver, gold, and gems." If indeed the land of Simbar does exist, it must lie beyond Temesia, an island supposedly haunted by Panic Demons. This alone might provide sufficient motivation to avoid traversing the seas which lie between Simbar and Talislanta. Some believe that the legendary kingdom of Acimera is to be found in this region.

TEMESIA: Temesia is a large island believed to be located somewhere in the Sea of Madness. According to one account, written by the popular Zandir poet, Rajni Rajim, the isle is "hung in mist, and covered in blue jungle. Silver dragonflies glide above the isle, and metallic blue irontrees sway in the wind; their clanging, clashing leaves sending showers of crimson sparks into the night sky. Quicksilver streams flow swiftly down the sides of the Mountain of Brass, wherein live the inhabitants of Temesia: the horrid, one-eyed beings known as Panic Demons. On leathery wings they circle high above, seeking creatures of flesh and blood to feed upon. Their inhuman, shrieking cries rend the air, traveling for miles on the wind. To hear the call of the Panic Demons, it is said, is to know the meaning of fear."

ALHAMBRA: West beyond the waters of the Azure Ocean is believed to lie the fabled land of Alhambra, a place mentioned in many of the most ancient Talislantan legends. Accounts vary greatly concerning the nature of Alhambra's inhabitants: some claim that sub-elementals (creatures of ice, mud, smoke, mist, or some other elemental substance) originate from this region. Others say that two great nations, called Randun and Kharistan, are to be found here. It is said that the two countries war against each other ceaselessly, and will one day succeed in completely annihilating each other. An old folk tale, which may or may not be true, describes Alhambra as "a land of smoke-grey hills and plains. Slugs and beetles, some as large and squat as wagons, slither across the bleak landscape. Below the ground live the Undermen: blind subterraneans, white as ghosts, with yellow claws and fangs. They hide in shallow holes, waiting to snare luckless creatures with their pole-hooks and drag them far below ground."

SEAS, OCEANS, RIVERS, AND LAKES

THE AZURE OCEAN: A wide expanse of deep-blue water, the Azure Ocean lies to the southwest of the Talislantan continent. Though its far southern reaches remain largely unknown, the Azure is otherwise the most traveled of Talislanta's seas and oceans. Zandir and Aamanian merchant ships, Imrian slave vessels, and the sea-rogues of Gao-Din all are known to frequent these waters. On rare occasions, Thaecian pleasure barges or sea nomads from Oceanus may be encountered. Storm demons are distressingly common during the spring and fall months, less so during other times of the year.

THE FAR SEAS: Situated to the southeast of Talislanta, the Far Seas are also well-traveled. They are considered dangerous due to the presence of Mangar corsairs, sea-demons and other malefic entities. As the black-hulled ships of the Black Savants of Nefaratus will allow passage through their territorial waters only to Imrian vessels, ships headed to Quan must take the longer and more hazardous open-sea routes. Golden-sailed dragon barques patrol the Quan coasts, seeking out smugglers, corsairs, and others who might pose some threat to the interests of the Quan Empire.

THE INLAND SEA: The Inland Sea is a large and scenic body of water located in the central regions of the Quan Empire. Slaves of the Empire pole these waters in search of moonfish, a delicacy deemed suitable only for the refined palates of the ruling class Quan. Kang sentinels patrol the shores of the Inland Sea, keeping a keen eye out for poachers. The coral city of Isalis, home of the Sunra, lies at the center of the Inland Sea.

THE LOST SEA: Once known as the Northern Sea, the Lost Sea is a flat expanse of wasteland ringed by the mountains of Narandu and Yrmania. The demise of the Northern Sea occurred sometime around the beginning of the Age of Confusion, the cause of this calamity remaining a source of heated debate among Talislantan scholars. Arguments range from the "crack in the world theory" (through which the waters of the sea seeped away) to the idea that advancing hordes of Ice Giants froze all the sea's tributaries, thus causing it to dry up. Whatever its origins, the Lost Sea is a strange region, littered with half-sunken ships and the bones of ancient sea dragons. Its former tributaries have also gone dry (see *The Dead River*).

THE MIDNIGHT SEA: A dark and ominous stretch of water, the Midnight Sea is located to the northwest of the Talislantan mainland. Those who travel its waters are few in number, and with good reason: ancient sea dragons lie sleeping beneath the waves, patiently awaiting their next meal. Sailors who have braved the Midnight Sea claim that phantom ships from the long-dead Kingdom of Khazad ply the ink-black waters, their spectral crews doomed to wander for all eternity.

THE SEA OF GLASS: Located in Faradun, the Sea of Glass is not a body of water, but a flat expanse of fused, green glass. The Cymrilians operate a mining installation on the western "shore" of the "sea." Otherwise, few bother to come here.

THE SEA OF ICE: An ever-frozen body of water, the Sea of Ice is considered part of L'Haan. The Mirin "sail" across the Sea of Ice on ice schooners equipped with long, adamantine-plated runners.

THE SEA OF MADNESS: A turbulent and seemingly malevolent body of water situated to the northeast of the Talislantan continent, the Sea of Madness lies beyond the territorial waters of the Quan Empire. Few ships dare to venture into these waters, which are said to be subject to strange and inexplicable phenomena: raging storms of black lightning, maelstroms, spiraling columns of water, and other less easily defined occurrences. Sea dragons and other frightening creatures are likewise rumored to prowl these waters. There is a legend to the effect that a large island, known as Temesia, lies at the furthest reaches of the Sea of Madness (see THE UNKNOWN LANDS).

THE SEA OF SORROW: A sizeable body of water almost entirely surrounded by land, the Sea of Sorrow is named for the many thousands of men lost long ago in sea battles between the Zandir and Aamanians. It is now a bustling waterway, used primarily by the merchant vessels of both nations. The hulks of sunken warships and merchants (many holding valuable treasures) litter the sea bed, and are a lure to salvage-men, scavengers, and adventurous sorts.

FROZEN LAKES: These ice-bound lakes—named Lahsa, Myr, Rhin, Y'Lal, and Lir —are all located in the far northern land of L'Hann. The blue-skinned Mirin peoples often engage in ice-fishing on these lakes, employing double-bladed ice skiffs as a means of transport across the frozen expanses.

LAKE VENDA: Source of the Axis River, Lake Venda lies at the foot of the Onyx Mountains in Arim. Fed by numerous small streams and brooks, its waters are cold and clear. Despite its seemingly peaceful appearance, the lake is avoided by the Arimites, who claim it to be cursed. According to legend, Lake Venda is inhabited by nine great Shaitan. They live in the ruins of an ancient, sunken city, and prey upon unwary sailors and fishermen. Each is said to possess a fabulous treasure: one of the Nine Keys of Knowledge, or one of the Devil-Rings of Oriax, depending upon which of the many conflicting accounts one wishes to believe.

LAKE ZEPHYR: Lake Zephyr is a beautiful and placid body of water located in Astar of the Seven Kingdoms. Many of Astar's Muses live around the lake, which is considered a capitol of sorts. The thaumaturges of Carantheum come here to purchase water, which is magically transmuted to solid blocks and shipped to the eastern deserts.

THE AXIS RIVER: A slate-grey river that flows slowly from the Onyx Mountains of Arim to the Azure Ocean, the Axis is heavily traveled by traders from Arim, Aaman and the Seven Kingdoms. Barges loaded with Arimite ores ply the river to the north, while the tiny cogs and punts of the Jhangarans and the barge forts of the Blue Ardua are most numerous along the southern end. Though very wide, the Axis River is quite shallow in spots. Only small or flat-bottomed craft can navigate its entire length in safety. Dozens of small tributaries of the Axis River run through the Swamplands of Mog, a branch of the Axis forming the southern border of the Seven Kingdoms.

THE DEAD RIVER: The Dead River was once the greatest waterway on the continent, until its source, the Northern Sea, inexplicably went dry (see *The Lost Sea*). It is now a winding chasm which extends some miles and nearly bisects the whole of Talislanta.

Forming a natural boundary line from Urag to Faradun, the crevasse ranges in depth from about fifty to two hundred feet. It is bridged at several points, the most reliable of which include Sindar and Kasmir of the Seven Kingdoms and Danuvia. The Dead River is shallowest in Urag and to the south, where crossings suitable for wagons and mounts can sometimes be found. In numerous places, it can only be forded on foot, a task requiring some skill in the art of rock climbing. The chasm forms a natural trail, however, and may be traversed throughout much of its length without great difficulty.

THE NECROS RIVER: The Necros River runs from the mountains of Khazad through the western forests of Werewood, emptying into the ocean at the Zandu border. The river forms a boundary of sorts, separating Werewood from the woodlands of Silvanus. Wood and rope bridges, most erected by the Sarista tribes, span the river at various points. The waters of the Necros, which originate from the eerie land of Khazad, are believed to be unsafe to drink. Some claim that more than a sip or two will cause the drinker to experience terrifying nightmares.

THE RIVER SHAN: The River Shan flows south from the northern coast of Quan to the Inland Sea, through Chana, and into the Far Seas. Narrow and treacherous at its southernmost end, the Shan is generally traveled only by Sunra fishing vessels and the pleasure craft and dragon barques of the Quan Empire.

THE SASCASM RIVER: The Sascasm flows from the Sardonyx Mountains of Yrmania through Werewood and Zandu. Slow moving and murky, the Sascasm divides in Werewood, one arm of the river terminating west of Arim in most unusual fashion: the waters simply disappear into a great sinkhole known as the Dead Lagoon. Lurkers and other insidious creatures dwell in the lagoon, which is strenuously avoided by reasonable folk. According to an old Dhuna legend, this part of the Sascasm does not actually terminate at the Dead Lagoon, but merely goes underground, its hidden tributaries flowing on for many miles. While most scholars denounce the Dhuna tale as pure nonsense, others consider this purported network of underground rivers, lakes, and grottos to be within the realm of possibility.

THE SYLVAN RIVER: Flowing south from Zephyr Lake in Astar, the Sylvan River winds its way through the Swamps of Mog and into the Gulf of Rajanistan. The waterway is difficult for any but the smallest craft to navigate, this due to a proliferation of tangled roots, silt deposits, and chunks of flotsam. Lurkers, poisonous snakes, and other unsavory creatures are likewise a deterrent to sensible travelers.

HISTORY OF TALISLANTA

The history of Talislanta, I am afraid to say, is somewhat less than certain, particularly as concerns the land's distant past. The reason for the distinct lack of reliable data regarding ancient times can probably be attributed to the occurrence of a most unfortunate event, referred to by Talislantan scholars as "the Great Disaster" (or, less commonly, "the Fatal Miscalculation," "Rodinn's Blunder," "the Unconscionable Oversight," and so forth). The cause of the Great Disaster remains a source of heated debate among Talislantan scholars. The most common explanations include a terrible war between the two ancient kingdoms of Sursia and Acimera, a combination of plagues, natural disasters, and other misfortunes, or the ill-advised tamperings of an incompetent wizard named Rodinn (see **WILDERLANDS OF ZARAN**; The Aberrant Forest).

Whatever its cause (or causes), the Great Disaster brought a swift end to what is now appropriately referred to as the Forgotten Age, eradicating all traces of this ancient era save for the seemingly countless ruins and desolate regions found to this day throughout much of the Talislantan continent.

As for the rest of Talislantan history: I have endeavored to construct a brief chart illustrating the chronology of various events deemed significant by those scholars whom I chanced to encounter in my travels. All dates are based upon the ancient Phaedran calendar, the Phaedrans having been among the first folk to again attain a relative degree of civilization following the Great Disaster. It is true that the Ariane of Altan are an older race, but their method of time-keeping (involving the positions of Talislanta's two suns and seven moons, among countless other, marginally relevant factors) is perhaps a bit too esoteric for the casual reader to appreciate, to say nothing of comprehend. The Mazdak, eastern contemporaries of the Phaedrans, were too occupied with killing each other to have taken much interest in the procession of historical events, and so are of little help to the hopeful chronicler of Talislantan history.

YEAR EVENT

"The Time Before Time" (also known as "The Age of Mystery"): Practically nothing is known of this ancient era, which immediately preceded "the Forgotten Age" and the Great Disaster. Some scholars claim that the mysterious civilization of Khazad, whose ruins still litter northwestern Talislanta, dates back to this period. Others believe that the massive structure known as the Watchstone was built during this time by a now-extinct race of giants.

? "The Forgotten Age": Rise and subsequent fall of the first known Talislantan civilizations. Names most often bandied about by scholars, all presumed to represent nations and peoples extant during this era, include: Elande, Sharna, Xambria, Pompados, Ashann, Phandril, Zaran, and infamous Sursia and Acimera, among others. Races such as the Gryphs, Gnomekin, Darklings, Imrians, Ice Giants, Mirin, and Ariane may have been in the process of establishing primitive settlements when the Great Disaster occurred, effectively bringing to a close this otherwise promising epoch. Artifacts from the Forgotten Age are eagerly sought after by scholars and collectors, even the most mundane curios bringing up to one hundred times their intrinsic value in some cases.

? = 0 "The Age of Confusion": A period during which the survivors of the Great Disaster scattered in all directions, abandoning the central regions (including the Red Desert and Wilderlands of Zaran, where the worst destruction seems to have taken place). An untold number of years passed before various races and peoples began again to establish settlements. In the west, the Phaedran tribes united and drove the Wildmen northwards beyond the Sardonyx Mountains of Yrmania. The Ur clans fled Narandu, seeking escape from the Ice Giants. In the east, the barbaric Mazdak tribes waged war upon each other ceaselessly, much to the relief of other neighboring clans. Most of the races of men showed a talent for procreation, and little else. The Ariane maze-city of Altan, created by Trans-Ascendant magics during the long years following the Great Disaster, was the only thriving settlement in the central region.

1 Beginning of "The New Age": The city state of Phaedra is established. The Orthodoxist and Paradoxist cults vie for control of the new state, but moderates choose the wizard Soliman III to be the first ruler of Phaedra. A period of prosperity follows, lasting some hundred and ten years.

21 The Mirin of L'Haan build the ice cities of L'Lal and Rhin.

29 The nomadic Dracartan tribes settle in the Red Desert, a region considered inhospitable by most other peoples. In the same year, they discover vast deposits of red iron. Djaffir merchants establish a trade route to Phaedra and work is begun on the city of Dracarta.

48 The Mazdaks finally kill each other off, leaving the barbaric Quan tribes in control of their old territories.

67 The Darkling hordes of Urag, fleeing the Ur clans, invade the territories of the Gnomekin. The Gnomekin hide underground until daybreak, then emerge in force and drive the Darklings back to their own shadowy lands. Called the One Day War, the incident promotes considerable laughter amongst the Gnomekin for months to come.

71 Soliman III, ruler of Phaedra, succumbs to old age. A period of mourning lasting twenty years is decreed by his successor, the magician Damon.

77 Phaedrans annex territories occupied by the Ardua, who flee to the forests of Vardune.

82 The Quan conquer the Vajra "Pangolin-People."

91 End of the twenty years' mourning in Phaedra. Damon decrees a twenty year period of celebration to follow, but is clapped in irons and branded a lunatic. Orthodoxists and Paradoxists again vie for power, but the sorcerer Kabros is chosen to rule Phaedra. Privately, he tells friends that the city state of Phaedra is on the verge of collapse, and advises against making long-term plans regarding the acquisition of property, among other things.

97 Imrian vessels raid the Dark Coast for the first time, taking many slaves.

100 Religious uprisings rock the capitol of Phaedra on the city state's 100th anniversary. The sorcerer Kabros resigns as ruler. In a stirring speech to his supporters (primarily magicians, wizards, and other sorcerers) Kabros advises them to consider "an exit, and a hasty one at that." By the following morning, he is sipping nectar on the Isle of Thaecia. Fearing for their lives, his advisors disguise one of their number as Kabros, successfully maintaining this ruse for over eleven years.

107 The Quan, utilizing Vajra engineers and laborers, dam the River Shan, forcing the Sunra to surrender. Using Sunra vessels, the Quan take the Mandalan city of Jacinth just one month later.

111 Kabros' advisors, their trickery finally uncovered, are forced to flee for their lives. The Orthodoxists seize control of the state, ordering dissidents to be incarcerated in the wilderness penal colony of Gao-Din. Beginning of the Cult Wars with the Paradoxists.

119 The Ur clans of Urag conquer and enslave the Darklings, then join forces with the avian Stryx.

122 The Quan bribe the Kang warchieftains, and establish the Quan Empire. The capitol city of Tian is built by conquered Mandalans and Vajra, and the Empire begins to prosper.

133 The penal colony of Gao is abandoned by the Phaedrans, and the Rogue City of Gao-Din is established soon afterwards.

146 Exiled Phaedran spell casters establish the free state of Cymril. Treaties are signed with the Thralls of Taz and the Gnomekin of Durne. The Farad establish a settlement in Faradun.

158 The Arimites build the ramshackle mining installation of Shattra, and declare this to be the capitol of the nation of Arim.

161 Za bandits and Beastmen contend for the border regions of Zaran.

176 Ice Giants attack L'Haan, but are driven back by the Mirin, who have discovered the secret of making adamant.

188 Mandalan mystics escape from Quan and flee into the Opal Mountains. Most are slain by Harakin tribesmen and Frostweres, but a few survive the journey and find the Temple of Xanadas. The Farad build the port city of Tarun.

193 Beastmen launch attacks against the settlements of the Sindar and Kasmir. Beginning of the Beast Wars.

207 The Dracartans of Carantheum re-discover the lost art of thaumaturgy.

222 The Kasmir, Sindarans, and Ardua sign treaties with the Cymrilian alliance. At the last minute, the Muses of Astar also decide to sign, and the confederation of states known as the Seven Kingdoms is established. The Beastmen beat a hasty retreat across the Plains of Golarin.

231 Kang drive the Nagra tribes out of Quan.

237 The Arimites, having become wealthy by supplying black iron to the warring Phaedran cultists, build the citadel of Akbar.

245 Gryphs from the forests of Tamaranth, suffering from a plague of gange, are cured by the magics of the Ariane. The Gryphs never forget this act of kindness from the strange folk of the Maze-City, vowing always to remain the protectors of the Ariane race.

267 Imrian slavers attempt to sack the Rogue City of Gao, but are repulsed. Hereafter, the Sea-Rogues harass Imrian vessels at every opportunity.

292 Sea Nomads build the floating city of Oceanus.

300 Jhangarans build settlements at Karansk and Tabal.

318 The Ur clans invade Yrmania.

321 Shabul, king of Arim, slain by Revenant Cultists.

334 The Ur, mired in a long and pointless war with the Wildmen of Yrmania, withdraw in disgust to their homeland.

350 Imrian slavers first encounter the Black Savants of Nefaratus. After losing many vessels, the Imrians strike a secret deal, and are thereafter allowed to pass (by specified routes only) through Nefaratan waters. Beginning of slave trade with the Quan Empire. The Mirin of L'Haan repulse an invading army of barbaric Harakin.

366 Thousands die in a bloody sea battle waged by opposing cult forces for control of the Phaedran Gulf. Hereafter, the gulf is known as the Sea of Sorrow.

383 Armies of the Quan plunge north into Harak, hoping to establish a safe route to L'Haan, rich in blue diamonds and adamant. Fierce bands of Harakin, mounted on winged dractyls, oppose them every step of the way. Finally, the Quan turn back, convinced that the prize is not worth the effort.

400 Xanadas leaves his followers, vowing on his death bed to return after visiting with the gods. Beginning of "The Long Wait."

404 Nomads of Rajanistan united under the Necromancer, Urmaan, after a series of drawn-out desert campaigns. Employing slave labor, the Rajans build the fortified citadel of Irdan.

422 Kang forces turn back an army of Witchmen from Chana. Beginning of the Quan Border Wars.

432 Saurans from the Volcanic Hills invade Quan. Mounted on armored land dragons, the Saurans advance slowly but inexorably towards the capitol of Tian. Only the early onset of winter stops the Saurans, cold weather forcing them to return to their more temperate homeland. Immediately following this disastrous incident, the emperor of Quan orders the swift construction of fortified border outposts and heavy siege engines as insurance against further assaults.

433 The Sauran armies return in the spring, but are unable to penetrate the Quan's new and hastily constructed defenses. Dismayed, the Saurans return to the Volcanic Hills.

444 Sheiks of the Djaffir bandit tribes arrive in Carantheum. They report that Urmaan of Rajanistan is amassing a great army of slave-warriors along the southern borders of the Wilderlands, presumably in preparation for an assault on the citadel of Dracarta. Abas the Grey, a thaumaturge noted for his quick wit, tells the Djaffir he "should appreciate Ahriman better were he to amass an army of slave girls instead." Not amused, the Djaffir hurl Abas out a window to his death. The Dracartans get the point, and promise to keep a close watch on the situation.

445 Armies of the Rajans launch an attack on Dracarta, the southernmost of Carantheum's outposts. The Dracartans, warned in advance by the Djaffir sheiks, annihilate the Rajan armies with relative ease. When news of the crushing defeat reaches Tarun, Urmaan has his entire staff of generals boiled in oil. Urmaan then disappears, never to be heard from again. A high priest of Rajanistan uses the incident to his advantage, claiming that Urmaan has gone to visit the entity known as Death, from whom he seeks advice and guidance on how to defeat the people of Carantheum. The idea so catches the fancy of the gullible Rajan populace that Death becomes the nation's patron "deity." A morbid cult springs up around the high priest, who becomes the first Khadun (mystic ruler) of the Rajans.

451 The Seven Kingdoms build the Seven Roads, encouraging trade between each of the member nations.

476 Death of the first Khadun of Rajanistan by unknown causes. The new Khadun claims his predecessor has "gone to seek Urmaan." The Rajan death cultists are thereafter known as the "Followers of Urmaan."

480 Independent city states of Danuvia, Maruk and Hadj are built by Phaedran exiles.

493 Ice Giants enter the forests of Tamaranth, and find the Ariane High Masters waiting for them. Employing their potent magics, the Ariane hasten the often slow process of spiritual ascendency, enabling the invading Ice Giants to immediately enter into their next incarnations as puddles of water.

500 The Rajans, led by the Khadun himself, attack Dracarta in force. Routed by the Dracartan's dune ships, the Rajans are torn to pieces as they flee madly across the desert sands. The Khadun is captured alive and plated with red iron by Dracarta's thaumaturges. His statue-like form is displayed in the capitol of Carantheum, where it decorates the Royal Palace. The battle comes to be known as the Massacre at Dracarta.

511 Exhausted after four hundred years of continuous warfare, the Orthodoxist and Paradoxist cults declare a truce. After a brief council, they agree to divide the old Phaedran territories into two separate nations: Zandu, to the west, becomes home to the Paradoxists. Aaman, to the east, is occupied by the Orthodoxists. Construction is begun on the Great Barrier Wall.

518 The Great Barrier Wall is completed, the Zandir and Aaman working together to erect this massive structure in only seven years.

538 Fierce Mangar corsairs begin to harass the dragon barques of the Quan Empire.

553 Ur clans from Urag pour into the gorge at Akbar, but are unable to penetrate the Arimites' strong defenses. They fall back to make new plans.

570 Imrians raid Mog for slaves, and sail upriver as far as Astar in search of Muses. They find an army of Thralls from Taz instead, and are driven down the Axis River and into the Azure Ocean. In the same year a large contingent of Imrians attempt to take the Isle of Thaecia, but are easily repulsed by the magics of the Thaecian enchanters.

600 Tamerlin writes his Chronicles of Talislanta.

SYNOPSIS OF TAMERLIN'S TRAVELS

The following is an outline of Tamerlin's travels across the continent of Talislanta. Due to the greatly disorganized condition of the wizard's notes and folios, an accurate and complete chronology of events regarding this period may be deemed a practical impossibility.

1) Tamerlin arrives in Talislanta. A stranger in a strange land, he mistakes Aaman for the ancient kingdom of Phaedra, and unknowingly commits a series of indiscretions which earn him the enmity of the Aamanian theocracy. Forced to flee for his life, the wizard accepts a five-year term of indentured servitude to an Arimite caravan master. He is smuggled out of Ammahd in the dead of night.

2) Tamerlin, working as an indentured caravan driver, tours Arim. His caravan stops at the citadel of Akbar, where the wizard views firsthand an attack by the monstrous Ur clans of neighboring Urag. In the ensuing confusion and activity, Tamerlin commandeers a steed and makes a discreet exit into the surrounding hills.

3) Some weeks later, Tamerlin arrives in Zanth, capitol of Zandu. He meets Orianos, a swashbuckling sea-farer who regales the wizard with tales of his dashing exploits. For a short time, Tamerlin stays in Zanth, earning a living by working as a professional seer and mystic. Prior circumstances in Aaman and Arim cause him to revise his plans; setting aside his fear of waterborne travel, the wizard obtains passage on a Zandir merchant ship headed to Faradun.

4) Enroute to Faradun, the Zandir vessel is set upon by sea-rogues from the Isle of Gao-Din. It is uncertain whether or not Tamerlin is surprised to learn that the pirates' captain is Orianos. After divesting all passengers of their valuables, the sea-rogues allow the Zandir ship to continue on to Faradun.

5) Tamerlin arrives in the port city of Tarun, in Faradun. Much to his surprise, the wizard is given a lavish reception and escorted to the manse of a wealthy Farad monopolist. Here, Tamerlin realizes that his good fortune has come about as a result of a case of mistaken identity. Deeming an undignified exit to be preferable to the machinations of Farad justice, the wizard flees the port city.

6) Good fortune visits Tamerlin, and he is befriended by a Phantasian dream merchant. Enroute to Zandu, a tragic accident occurs, leaving Tamerlin to pilot the Phantasian's windship by himself.

7) Tamerlin is forced to make an unscheduled landing on the isle of Thaecia. He visits the Festival of the Bizarre, trading the Phantasian's cargo of dream essences for various curios and magical adjuncts before again setting sail for Zandu.

8) A storm blows Tamerlin's windship off course. Hopelessly lost, he lands the vessel on the outskirts of Cymril of the Seven Kingdoms. Here he meets the magician, Crystabal, who is also headed for Zandu. The two depart together in Tamerlin's windship.

9) A mishap involving a potent magical artifact leads to the untimely destruction of the windship. Tamerlin and Crystabal are inadvertently separated. For a time, the wizard's whereabouts remain unknown; it is thought that the erstwhile scholar may have spent several months traveling in the guise of a charlatan or quack doctor.

10) Tamerlin resurfaces in Sindar of the Seven Kingdoms, where he has come to sell artifacts. He meets the Ariane known as Shadowmoon, who offers to guide Tamerlin across the Wilderlands of Zaran. The wizard accepts, and the two set off to the east.

11) Tamerlin explores the Wilderlands with Shadowmoon. Though details of this period are scarce, it is generally believed that the two travelers crossed the Lost River at Sindar and cut across the Plains of Golarin, where it is likely that they explored certain of the ruined cities which litter this region. From there, a brief stop at the city state of Maruk would seem to have been indicated, after which the two disappeared into the northeastern wastelands.

12) Tamerlin, with Shadowmoon, visits L'Haan.

13) Tamerlin follows Shadowmoon to Narandu. After this trip, the two part company at the border of Sindar.

14) Tamerlin travels to Cymril. Here he again meets Crystabal, who has come to be known in Cymril as "the rogue magician." They spend long days together, partaking of the finest foods and wines, and engaging in lengthy discussions concerning their future plans. Soon neither has any money left. In order to eat, Tamerlin and Crystabal take work with a penurious Kasmir money lender, who offers to finance an expedition to Mog in order to acquire a shipment of costly magical herbs. Tamerlin, by virtue of his experience, is assigned to lead the group. Included in their number is Ramm, a Thrall warrior hired to serve as the party's guide.

15) Tamerlin and his party travel to the Swamplands of Mog. They purchase the herbs as instructed, but take pity on the dull-witted Mogroth, whom the Kasmir financier intended to cheat. Tamerlin pays a fair price to the Mogroth, choosing instead to renege on his contract with the Kasmir. The wizard and rogue magician decide to make for Tabal, in Jhangara, from whence they hope to obtain passage to Zandu. Perplexed, Ramm returns back home to Taz of the Seven Kingdoms.

16) Enroute to Tabal, Tamerlin and Crystabal are taken by Imrian slavers. They are rescued by a band of sea-rogues from the Isle of Gao-Din, led by the estimable Orianos. On orders from their captain, the sea-rogues convey Tamerlin and Crystabal to the coasts of Silvanus.

17) Tamerlin, with Crystabal, visits the Sarista gypsy peoples. The rogue magician convinces the wizard to accompany him on a quest to locate the Lost City of the Dead in Khazad.

18) The quest to Khazad ends in frustration. Crystabal and Tamerlin part company; the rogue magician retiring to the city of Zanth, while Tamerlin, instilled with wanderlust, travels alone to the Zandir outpost of Zandre. Here, the wizard meets Tane, a mercenary Jaka hunter.

19) Tamerlin and Tane go forth into the forests of Werewood in search of the tomb of an ancient Phaedran wizard. Logistical difficulties force a temporary postponement of their ultimate goal, necessitating the formulation of a new strategy.

20) Tamerlin convinces a reluctant Tane to accompany him on a hazardous voyage to the Lost Sea, in Yrmania. They endure great hardships, but uncover a rich cache of sunken treasure, and so are rewarded for their efforts. Taking as much of the booty as their mounts can bear, the two adventurers turn to the south and make for the Zandu border.

21) Tamerlin and Tane return to the border outpost of Zandre. The wizard, with his new-found wealth, makes preparations for a sojourn to the eastern lands. Tane declines to attend, citing pressing business in Arim. The two go their separate ways.

22) Tamerlin, in the guise of a curio dealer, ventures forth on a journey that will take him to the far corners of the Talislantan continent. Little is known of his travels until he reaches Dracarta.

23) Following an ill-advised expedition into the Red Desert, Tamerlin joins up with a nomadic tribe of Djaffir merchants. The Djaffir, with the wizard in tow, make for the citadel of Hadran on the Quan border.

24) Having survived an encounter with the hostile armies of Rajanistan, Tamerlin and the Djaffir cross the bridge at Hadran and enter the land of Quan. The nomads sell their wares and make ready to return to Djaffa, but Tamerlin obtains a merchants' visa, allowing him to travel the Emperor's Road to the northern sectors of Quan.

25) Tamerlin is taken to Tian, capitol of Quan, by a troop of elite Kang warriors. Here, the wizard learns that he has been chosen to travel the length and breadth of Quan at the behest of the Emperor of Quan. Zen, a charming Mandalan savant enslaved by the Quan, is assigned to be Tamerlin's guide. Twenty elite Kang warriors accompany them, affording a grim reminder of the involuntary nature of their assignment. For the next three years, the wizard explores the far corners of the empire, compiling notes and collecting various sorts of curios and artifacts along the way.

26) An incident involving the Witchmen of Chana allows Tamerlin and Zen to terminate their respective arrangements with the Quan Empire. Without delay they head westwards. A long and arduous journey follows, the details of which seem somehow to have been omitted (or deleted) from Tamerlin's notes. It is logical to suppose that the wizard and his female companion made their way to Anasa, or perhaps Hadj; from there, the two may have crossed the Dead River at Danuvia or Kasmir, heading west across the Seven Kingdoms. On the other hand, one cannot rule out the possibility that Tamerlin's escape was facilitated in some way by magic.

27) Tamerlin and Zen arrive in Zanth, the capitol of Zandu. The wizard is reunited with the rogue magician Crystabal, and the three discuss future plans over many a glass of Zandir wine.

GLOSSARY OF TALISLANTAN TERMS

Aamanian: A citizen of Aaman. Colloquially, a derogatory term meaning "fanatic," "prudish," or "intolerant," depending on the context in which the word is used.

Ahazu: Any of a race of four-armed, warlike savages native to the Eastern Junglelands of the Dark Coast.

Ahtra: A species of burden beast bred by the nomadic Djaffir tribes of Djaffa. There are three sub-species of Ahtra: the one-humped Ontra, the two-humped Batra, and the three-humped Tatra.

Amberglass: A fine glass derived from raw amber or amber crystal, having many practical applications in various magical, alchemical and thaumaturgical operations.

Aquavit: An effervescent liquor popular in Cymril of the Seven Kingdoms.

Araq: A sorcerous crossbreed of Sauran and man, generally exhibiting the worst traits of these two races.

Ardua: A species of former avians, now in the process of "devolving" into a race of ground-dwellers. There are two sub-species: the smaller Green Ardua, and the larger Blue Ardua. Both retain vestigial wings and head-crests of bright, metallic-hued plumes.

Ariane: A humanoid people dwelling within the Maze-City of Altan in Tamaranth, notable as practitioners of the metaphysical doctrines of Trans-Ascendancy (q.v.).

Arimite: A citizen of Arim. Elsewhere, the term is loosely used to describe any type of vicious cut-throat.

Armored Leech: Popular name for the Aramatus; a segmented, serpentine creature which dwells in bogs and sewers and feeds on carrion, refuse and—as the opportunity warrants—living prey.

Avar: The Farad's deity of wealth and personal gain, typically depicted as a golden idol with outstretched, grasping hands.

Azoryl: A species of winged reptilians native to the Sinking Land and neighboring regions.

Batrean: A race of primitive humanoids inhabiting the island of Batre. The females are alluring creatures of exceptional charm and beauty; the males, huge and repugnant monsters with a tendency towards violent behavior.

Bat Manta: A species of extra-dimensional creatures resembling giant manta rays. Categorized as lesser demons by some Talislantan scholars, Bat Manta are capable of flight, and are employed as steeds by certain black magicians.

Beastmen: A species of bestial humanoids native to the Plains of Golarin. Omnivorous creatures, Beastmen scavenge the numerous ruined cities and structures which dot the Plains region, traveling in large packs.

Black Pit of Narandu: Purportedly, a bottomless fissure located in the south-central region of Narandu, and the source of many colorful and imaginative legends.

Black Savant: Any of the mysterious inhabitants of the isle of Nefaratus; in popular conception, a race of diabolists.

Bodor: An amber-skinned, portly race of humanoids renowned as traveling musicians. A people displaced by the Great Disaster (q.v.).

Cadeucus: Magic wand and symbol of the Dracartan thaumaturges. The cadeucus is utilized in all thaumaturgic operations entailing the use of quintessence (q.v.).

Chana Witchmen/Witchwomen: Primitive inhabitants of the Jungles of Chana, and practitioners of various, grisly necromantic rituals.

Cral: Mercantile ruler and despot of Faradun.

Cymrilian: A citizen of Cymril, erstwhile capitol of the Seven Kingdoms. A green-skinned and green-haired people, the Cymrilians are enamored of all things magical.

Da-Khar: A type of hide gauntlet equipped with retractable claws. Da-Khar are favored by the Torquar (q.v.) of Rajanistan.

Danuvian: A citizen of the City State of Danuvia. Male Danuvians are typically weak and slack-witted; quite the opposite of the females, who are renowned as swordswomen, military tacticians and administrators.

Darkling: Any of a race of vile, skulking humanoids native to the Darklands of Urag.

Deadman: A rare species of plant, the deathly pale leaves of which exude a lethal contact poison.

Demon: Any of several species of extra-dimensional entities originating from the lower plane of Cthonia. Categorized as quasi-elementals by many Talislantan scholars, the most commonly-known demon types include Earth Demons, Frost Demons, Night Demons, Sand Demons, Sea Demons, Swamp Demons, and Wind Demons.

Devil: Any of several species of extra-dimensional beings originating from the lower planes of existence. The most commonly-known types include the Shaitan, Enim and Sardonicus (q.v.).

Devilroot: A rare species of plant with blue-black, "horned" leaves. The root of the plant, when dried and prepared in the proper fashion, yields a virulent toxin which is much favored for use by assassins.

Dhuna: A people related to the Sarista, reputed to have an obsessive interest in witchcraft. The kiss of a Dhuna witchwoman is credited in popular belief with the ability to enslave a man's heart.

Djaffir: A nomadic people native to the desert kingdom of Djaffa and its surrounding environs. The Djaffir population is divided into two main tribes: Merchants and Bandits. Critics maintain that distinctions between the two are minimal at best.

D'Oko: A large species of plant found only in the Rain Forests of the Dark Coast. The Green Men (q.v.) dwell within the D'Oko's hollow bole and protect the plant from harm, an arrangement constituting a unique form of symbiotic relationship.

Dracartan: A civilian of the desert kingdom of Carantheum, descended from the nomadic people of the same name.

Draconid: A diminutive species of pseudo-dragon native to the Volcanic Hills region. The Draconid's bite is poisonous.

Dractyl: A winged and ungainly species of reptilian native to the bleak land of Harak. The Harakin tribes utilize Dractyl as steeds, a situation dictated by need rather than choice.

Dragon: There are several species of Dragon native to the continent, including the ponderous Land Dragon, the aquatic Sea Dragon, the multi-headed Kaliya (or Black Dragon) and the giant Crested Dragon. With the possible exception of Land Dragons, the various species of Talislantan Dragon show a marked propensity for cunning, and even devious, behavior. Some few are believed to possess innate magical abilities, the Crested Dragon in particular.

Drukh: A tribe of primitive humanoids native to the mountainous regions of Arim, notable for their bloodthirsty and excessively violent tendencies.

Enim: A race of giant Devils (q.v.), some few of which are known to inhabit the Barrens and other sectors of the Wilderlands of Zaran. They enjoy violent sport and have a weakness for games of chance, gold and man-flesh.

Equus: A species of quadrupedal beasts found throughout various parts of the continent. Known sub-species include the cold-dwelling Snowmane, the swift Silvermane, the Greymane (much-valued for use as durable and loyal steeds) and the bestial Darkmane.

Exarch: Hereditary monarch of the Arimites, who dwells in seclusion within the walls of the Forbidden City of Ahrazad.

Farad: A citizen of Faradun. In Djaffa, the term carries unfavorable connotations, both literally and figuratively.

Ferran: A species of ferral humanoids native to the Wilderlands of Zaran. Ferrans live in underground tunnels, coming forth at dusk to scavenge for food or steal from unwary travelers.

Frostwere: An arctic species of Yaksha (q.v.), known to inhabit frozen tundra and high mountain ranges. Occasionally mistaken for Frost Demons by less-than-expert observers.

Gao-Din: A rocky isle situated off the southern coast of Mog; formerly a penal colony of the ancient Phaedran Dynasty, now home to the Rogue City of Gao.

Gnomekin: A race of smallish, brown-skinned humanoids native to the subterranean caverns and grottos of Durne.

Great Disaster: A cataclysmic occurrence—perhaps the inadvertent result of the Mad Wizard Rodinn's misguided attempts to concoct quintessence—which laid waste to much of the continent and brought to ruin the first great civilizations of Talislanta. The results of the Great Disaster are still in evidence throughout the Wilderlands of Zaran, a vast region littered with ruined cities and bizarre topographical and climatic anomalies.

Green Men: A race of diminutive plant people native to the Western Rain Forests of the Dark Coast. Peaceful symbionts, the Green Men live in complete harmony with their surroundings, and possess the ability to communicate with and influence all types of plantlife.

Greymane: See Equus.

Gryph: A race of avian·humanoids native to the forests of Tamaranth. They are aggressive protectors of their woodland home, and friends to the Ariane (q.v.).

Hadjin: A citizen of the City State of Hadj. The Hadjin are among the wealthiest folk in Talislanta, and consider themselves superior to the "common" people of other lands.

Harakin: A nomadic and warlike race native to the bleak and uninviting region known as Harak. Conditioned to withstand hardship, they are perhaps the ultimate survivalists.

Hierophant: High Priest of the Orthodoxist cult (q.v.) and ruler of Aaman.

Ice Giant: Monstrous humanoids whose bodies are comprised of magically animate ice. They dwell within the frozen expanses of Narandu.

Ice King: Mysterious ruler of the Ice Giants, purportedly a warlock of great power.

Ikshada: A species of armored parasites measuring up to twelve inches in length. There are three distinct sub-species: the tree-dwelling Yellow Ikshada, the aquatic Grey Ikshada, and the Black Ikshada, which haunts subterranean caverns and crypts.

Imrian: A race of brutish, amphibious humanoids native to the island of Imria. They travel the seas in coracles drawn by teams of Kra (q.v.), preying on the primitive peoples of the Azure Ocean region, whom they capture and sell as slaves.

Ironshrike: Smaller relative of the Shrieker (q.v.). Ironshrikes prey upon Ikshada, whose sting has no effect upon these metal-plumed avians.

Jabutu: A rare tropical plant found only in the Jungles of Chana. A derivative of the plant is used in the making of Kesh, a potent elixir with uncanny properties (q.v.).

Jaka: A race of furred humanoids native to the Brown Hills of Yrmania. They possess a type of sixth sense, and are skilled trackers and manhunters.

Jamba: Unknowable patron deity of the Dracartans, to whom Jamba supposedly gave the secrets of the Lost Art of Thaumaturgy.

Juju: An undead fetish-creature created through the use of Black Magic. A zombie, controlled by manipulation of a graven image.

Kabros: Legendary sorcerer-king of ancient Phaedra, renowned as the author of numerous cogent spells and insightful treatises on inter-dimensional travel. Considered a visionary, particularly after his timely escape from Phaedra just prior to the fall of the old dynasty.

Kaliya: **See Dragon.**

Kang: A warlike, crimson-skinned race, now fawning servitors of the Quan (q.v.).

Kasmir: A citizen of the desert kingdom of Kasmir. The shrivel-skinned Kasmir bear a reputation as shrewd money lenders and appraisers.

Kesh: A pungent liquid made from the root of the Jabutu plant. According to the quantity consumed, drinkers of Kesh claim to be capable of detecting invisible and spirit presences, to see into other planes of existence, or to actually enter other dimensions. The substance has potent hallucinogenic properties, which perhaps goes far to explain the claims of its users.

Khadun: Necromantic high priest and ruler of Rajanistan. The Khadun is viewed as an earthly manifestation of Death by his morbid followers, who willingly serve him without question.

Khu: A double-bladed dagger used by the Harakin tribes.

Krin: A heavy, black iron crossbow employed by the Harakin tribes. The Krin uses hammered iron spikes as ammunition, and is a cumbersome and unwieldy weapon.

K'Tallah: A potent narcotic substance which bestows upon the user the ability to see into the future. K'Tallah is in wide use in Rajanistan and, to a lesser extent, Faradun. It is highly addictive.

Lurker: Colloquial term for Sea Demon.

Mandalan: A race of passive, golden-skinned humanoids conquered and enslaved by the Quan (q.v.).

Mandragore: A species of insidious plant-creatures native to the forests of Werewood.

Mangar Corsair: Piratical denizens of the Mangars, a cluster of small islands situated in the Crescent Isles. The term applies as well to individuals of other races who, by choice or coercion, have joined up with the Corsairs.

Mangonel Lizard: A species of large reptile similar in some respects to Land Lizards, but having a muscular tail tipped with a rock-hard knob of bone and cartilage. The Mangonel Lizard's tail is an effective deterrent to predators, and is similarly employed in the creature's combative mating rituals.

Manik: Insane and chaotic patron deity of the Wildmen of Yrmania, whose bizarre behavior possibly reflects an attempt to emulate the purported nature of Manik himself.

Manra: A race of primitive humanoids native to the northern region of Chana. The Manra are shape-changers, possessing the ability to adopt the physical semblances of other lifeforms.

Maruk: A citizen of the Independent City State of Maruk. Victims of an age-old curse, the Maruk are widely regarded as harbingers of gloom and ill fortune, and accordingly are shunned by the more superstitious peoples of Talislanta.

Matsu: A type of long-handled warclub favored by the Ahazu tribes of the Dark Coast.

Megalodont: A giant, six-legged reptilian, native to the Plains of Golarin and parts of Urag and the Wilderlands. Megalodonts are herbivorous, and travel in herds of up to a hundred or more individuals. A stampeding Megalodont herd is a thing to be avoided at all costs.

Mirin: A race of blue-skinned humanoids native to the snowfields of L'Hann. The Mirin dwell in ice castles, and are ruled by the Snow Queen, a White Witch of great power.

Mogroth: A ponderous race of sloth-like humanoids native to the swamplands of Mog. In popular usage, the term has come to mean "slow," "dull-witted," or "dense."

Monolith: A race of mountainous beings whose bodies are comprised entirely of earth and stone. Monoliths dwell on the island of Gargantua in the Thaecian Isle chain, and may be the oldest living things in Talislanta.

Morphius: A parasitic plant found in swamps, marshes and lowlands. The deep blue blossoms of the Morphius exude a fragrance which induces sleep.

Mud People: A race of six-limbed, amphibious humanoids native to the Dark Coast. The Mud People live in above-ground tunnel-complexes constructed of sodden earth and mud (hence their name).

Muse: A race of butterfly-winged, nymph-like humanoids native to the sylvan glades of Astar. Muses are empaths, notable as artisans of superior skill and utterly lax work habits.

Muskront: Shaggy-haired relative of the Ogriphant (q.v.), hunted for its pungent musk and hide. Muskronts are foul-tempered, and dangerous when aroused to anger.

Na-Ku: A race of indigo blue-skinned pseudo-demons native to the island of Pana-Ku, of the Crescent Isles chain. Their ruler is a horrible half-demon, fattened on prisoners captured by the Na-Ku, who are cannibalistic by nature.

Nagra: A race of primitive, frightful-looking humanoids native to the Jade Mountains and surrounding areas. The Nagra are renowned as spirit-trackers, possessing the uncanny ability to follow the faint spirit emanations of living creatures.

Necron: Legendary "City of the Dead" in Khazad, where it is said that an entire city and its population is interred below the ground.

Nightstalker: Fearsome denizens of the Astral Plane, who invade the dreams and nightmares of living creatures, seeking to slay victims by devouring their astral forms.

Nocturnal Strangler: A mysterious, invisible creature rumored to inhabit Urag, Arim, and other neighboring locales.

Oc: A peculiar type of barbed bolas employed by Imrian slavers in order to capture prey.

Ogriphant: A species of massive, quadrupedal herbivores native to the western regions of Talislanta. Domesticated in some lands, Ogriphant are used as burden beasts, and to help clear forest or jungle land. Wild Ogriphant are hunted for their tusks.

Ogront: Ogronts are gigantic herbivores, towering over even the largest Megalodonts (q.v.). Practically mindless, these immense beasts are impervious to harm, and pose an incidental danger to outpost settlements and farms located in near proximity to their grazing and breeding grounds.

Omnival: Traditional name for the Orthodoxist cult's "Books of the Law;" a listing of acceptable customs, behaviorisms, modes of thought, proscriptions against infidels, and related cult doctrines.

Orthodoxist: A practitioner of Orthodoxy, the severe state religion of Aaman.

Paradoxist: A practitioner of Paradoxy, a quasi-mystical doctrine popular in the land of Zandu.

Phantasian: A race of tall, thin humanoids native to the isle of Phantas. The Phantasians are renowned as minor magicians and sellers of Dream Essence, the purported "stuff which dreams are made of."

Quan: Technically, any citizen of the Quan Empire. The term is more accurately used to describe the race of formerly barbaric humanoids who rule the Empire, known as the Quan.

Quintessence: A crystalline powder derived by thaumaturgic techniques, and having profound magical properties.

Rahastran: A race of wandering seers and mountebanks, skilled in the use of the Zodar, a card game used to divine the future.

Rajan: A saturnine race of humanoids; civilians of the Desert Kingdom of Rajanistan. The Rajans serve their ruler, the Khadun, whom they revere as the earthly manifestation of the dread entity, Death.

Raknid: A vile species of insectoids thought to be a hybrid of demon and giant scorpion, known to inhabit the Volcanic Hills region. An aquatic species, the Water Raknid, is also known to exist.

Revenant: Member of a secret society of assassins which operates freely in the land of Arim.

Rodinn: Legendary "Mad Wizard" of ancient times, whose ill-advised magical experiments inadvertently led to the creation of the Aberrant Forest, and may well have caused that singular catastrophe known in Talislantan history as the Great Disaster.

R'ruh: A sharp-edged stone disc affixed to a leather thong and employed as an axe and missile weapon by the Wildmen tribes of Yrmania.

Sardonicus: A vile species of imp-like minor devils favored as familiars and advisors by black magicians; also known as "bottle-imps."

Sarista: A dark-skinned race of gypsy people native to the woodlands of Silvanus. The Sarista bear a richly-deserved reputation as incorrigible thieves, con-men and charlatans.

Sauran: A species of large, reptilian humanoids native to the Volcanic Hills region. The Saurans are a warlike race, who have domesticated the monstrous creatures known as Land Dragons, which they employ in battle as living siege engines.

Saurud: A species of reptilian humanoid related to the Saurans (q.v.), but being more massive of build and generally slower-moving.

Sawilu: A species of translucent-skinned albinoids native to the island of Fahn in the Crescent Isles chain. The Sawilu are spell-weavers, skilled in the art of casting enchantments by the use of intricate songs.

Scourge: A type of giant siege engine employed by the Ur clans of Urag (q.v.), consisting of a thirty-foot rotating spindle, to which are affixed rows of spikes, rasps, scything blades and ball-tipped chains. A team of slaves operating winches sets the scourge in motion, the movement of its wheels causing the spindle to revolve with great force.

Shadinn: A race of giant humanoids related to the Rajans (q.v.).

Shadow Wizard: Spectral denizens of the Shadow Realm, rumored to be black magicians of terrible power. Most live in the Iron Citadel, an eerie structure surmounted by towers equipped with enchanted orbs of carved onyx.

Shaitan: A species of giant devils cast out from the heavens and consigned to dwell in a brass city situated amidst the lower plane of Oblivion. Their ruler, Diabolus, is a master of the Black Arts, and a creature purported to be horrible to behold.

Shrieker: A species of fierce, avian predators native to the Cerulean Forest of Quan and surrounding environs. Shriekers have metallic feathers, razor-sharp claws and long, pointed beaks; the latter, used to spear prey by diving down from the treetops.

Silvermane: See Equs.

Sindaran: A race of thin, seven-foot tall humanoids native to the mesalands of Sindar. The Sindarans are dual-encephalons; "double-brained" beings possessed of exceptional intellectual capabilities.

Skoryx: A type of alcoholic beverage favored by the folk of Sindar, among others. It is quite potent, but is most notable for its myriad and varying taste sensations, a quality derived from the use of rainbow lotus in the distillation process.

Smokk: An odd and ungainly species of flightless bird found only in certain parts of Urag. The Smokk possesses an uncanny talent for locating precious stones and metals, and as such is highly valued by prospectors and adventurers.

Snipe: A species of intelligent (and insatiably curious) mollusk native to the Sinking Land. The Snipe is able to pass swiftly through the mud and sludge of its homeland as a fish swims through the water; a useful ability when spying on other creatures or fleeing from voracious predators.

Snowmane: See Equs.

Strider: A species of large, bi-pedal predator resembling a cross between reptile and flightless bird. The Kang (q.v.) employ trained Striders as warsteeds; in the wild, the creatures are vicious, and prone to mad attacks. A swamp-dwelling species, the Marsh Strider, is also known to exist.

Sunra: A race of silvery-skinned, semi-aquatic humanoids; subjects of the Quan (q.v.). The Sunra live in the Coral City of Isalis, build magnificent Dragon Barques, and are the most skilled navigators on the continent.

Stryx: A race of foul avian humanoids native to the Obsidian Mountains and other areas in Urag. The Stryx are carrion-eaters, who scavenge battlefields and burial mounds for food.

Tantalus: A leafy plant, the heart-shaped root of which is dried and crushed to obtain a powder (also called Tantalus) reputed to have aphrodisiac properties.

Tarak: A heavy, four-bladed iron axe employed by the Harakin tribes (q.v.).

Tarkus: A species of murderous, quadrupedal carnivores; possibly a sorcerous hybrid of mangonel lizard, raknid and Tundra Beast (q.v.). The Kang (q.v.) of Quan use trained Tarkus as hunting beasts.

Thaecian; A tall, slender and graceful people native to the isle of Thaecia. The Thaecians are skilled in the arts of Enchantment, and create many wondrous products and wares.

Thrall: A race of giant albinoids bred specifically for use as an army of slave warriors by the sorcerers of some ancient, and now forgotten, land. It is the practice of the Thralls to cover their bodies from head to foot with colorful and elaborate tattooes, this as a means of expressing individuality; aside from differences in gender, all Thralls would otherwise look exactly alike.

Tirshata: Fabled—and possibly mythical—future savior and ruler of the Za bandit tribes (q.v.).

Torquar: A secret society of torturers, assassins and terrorists, sworn to serve the Khadun of Rajanistan.

Trans-Ascendancy: A system of metaphysical theorisms and beliefs adhered to by the Ariane (q.v.), who believe that all creatures and things are animate, incarnating entities.

Trivarian: A complex game favored by the dual-encephalons of Sindar, but quite incomprehensible to non-Sindarans.

Tundra Beast: A particularly fierce, two-headed species of quadrupedal carnivore native to the northern regions of Talislanta.

Ur: A massive and malformed species of humanoid native to the wilds of Urag, having yellow-green skin, curved fangs and brutish features. The Ur clans dwell in rude stone fortresses and build giant siege engines, which they use in battle against their foes and rivals.

Vajra: A species of stout, subterranean humanoids whose sturdy frames are covered with rows of overlapping, scaly plates; subjects of the Quan (q.v.). The Vajra are renowned as skilled builders and engineers.

Vird: A mongrel race related to the Rajans (q.v.). Colloquially, the word serves as the basis for numerous derogatory remarks: "son of a Vird," "mother of a Vird," and so forth.

Vorl: An insidious species of beings whose bodies are comprised entirely of animate mists and vapors. Vorls subsist on the vital fluids of living creatures, which they drain by enveloping victims in their trailing, wispy forms.

Watchstone: A massive pinnacle of stone, carved into the face of which is a long, winding stairway. From the summit, one can see across the whole of Golarin. The obelisk-like structure is of some significance to the Orthodoxists of Aaman.

Weirdling: A nearly extinct race of diminutive, gnarled humanoids native to the dreary forests of Werewood. According to legend, a captured Weirdling must either yield its treasure-horde or grant its captor a wish (hence the popular name, "wish-gnomes").

Well of Saints: A magical well located in the Valley of Mists. Water from the Well of Saints is said to possess remarkable healing properties. The well is of significance to the Orthodoxists of Aaman (q.v.), as well as other, lesser-known religions. Some claim that a magical being or monster lives deep within the well, warding the enchanted waters from any who dare take more than the single, allotted sip.

Whisp: A diminutive species of pseudo-elementals native to various woodland and wilderland regions. Whisps are said to know magic of the most ancient sort, and can be both mischievous and cruel.

Whisperweed: A variety of wild grass which—quite mysteriously—whispers strange secrets when blown in the breeze.

Wildmen: A race of ape-like humanoids native to the Badlands of Yrmania. Ritual ingestion of death's angel, a toxic variety of mushroom, has rendered the primitive tribes quite insane.

Xambrian: Members of an advanced and peaceful people all but exterminated by the Quaranians, a race of black magicians and diabolists extant during ancient times. Descendants of the few surviving Xambrians typically work as wizard hunters, tracking down reincarnated Quaranians and bringing them to justice.

Xanadas: Fabled High Mystic and Master of a legendary group of hermits and savants, who left his followers to "visit with the Gods." His faithful followers (or, more likely, their descendants) continue to await the promised return of Xanadas, keeping safe his old dwelling place in the Temple of the Seven Moons.

Yaksha: A species of giant, bi-pedal carnivores native to the mountains of Arim and neighboring territories. Deemed the fiercest of Talislantan creatures, Yaksha are notably devoid of fear or reason, and have no natural enemies.

Yellow Aqueor: A variety of aquatic plant, similar to sea-kelp, which grows to immense size. The plant has many practical uses, and is a staple crop of the Sea Nomads of Oceanus.

Yitek: A race of tall, sombre humanoids native to the Wilderlands of Zaran and surrounding areas. A nomadic people, the Yitek earn a living as tomb robbers, a profession which endears them to few other Talislantans.

Za: A race of malign, nomadic humanoids native to the Wilderlands of Zaran. The Za bandit clans bear a reputation as blood-thirsty killers, and are held in low esteem throughout much of the continent.

Zagir: A race of wiry, dark-skinned humanoids related to the Rajans (q.v.).

Zandir: A citizen of Zandu. Elsewhere, a derogatory term meaning "philanderer," "cuckold," and so on.

Zaratan: A species of huge, aquatic reptilians native to the southern seas of Talislanta. Normally docile, Zaratan are the enemies of Sea Dragons and other large marine predators. The species has been domesticated by the Sea Nomads of Oceanus, who employ them as waterborne steeds and burden beasts.

THE TALISLANTAN HANDBOOK

THE TALISLANTAN HANDBOOK is the authoritative guide to fantasy role playing in the world of Talislanta. The book features over eighty different character types of all races and nationalities, plus detailed descriptions of Talislantan weapons, windships, duneships, currencies, languages, cults and secret societies, trade goods and much more. Also included is a complete and comprehensive game system which incorporates rules for combat, magic, and a wide variety of skills. If you're an experienced role player or Gamemaster and are getting a little tired of dwarves and halflings, **THE TALISLANTAN HANDBOOK** is for you.

THE TALISLANTAN HANDBOOK

FANTASY ROLE PLAYING GAME SUPPLEMENT

A NATURALIST'S GUIDE TO TALISLANTA

The **TALISLANTA** series continues with the **NATURALIST'S GUIDE,** a compendium of selected flora and fauna from the magical realm of Talislanta.

Compiled from the notes of Tamerlin—traveler, self-styled wizard and author of **THE CHRONICLES OF TALISLANTA,** the **NATURALIST'S GUIDE** features illustrations and descriptions for over a hundred different creatures and beings, including:

Ahazu: fierce, four-armed warriors from the jungles of the Dark Coast...

Exomorphs: predatory beasts feared for their uncanny, chameleon-like powers...

Gnomekin: diminutive, furry-maned humanoids who make their home in underground "nooks" and tunnels...

Monoliths: gigantic beings of earth and stone, believed to be the oldest livig entities in the world...

Sardonicus: evil geniuses known as "bottle-imps," favored as familiars and sorcerous advisors...

Snipes: an intelligent (and insatiably curious) species of mud-dwelling mollusk known to inhabit the Sinking Land...

Vorls: insidious creatures whose bodily forms are comprised of animate mists and vapors...

plus Mandragores, Shadow Wizards, Nightstalkers, Werebeasts, and many, many more...

With a separate section for fantasy role players featuring game statistics and additional information.

A NATURALIST'S GUIDE TO

TALISLANTA

By Stephan Michael Sech

Illustrated by P.D. Breeding

FANTASY ROLE PLAYING GAME SUPPLEMENT